Animal Instincts

Russell Freedman
and
James E. Morriss

Holiday House, Inc.

New York

Grateful acknowledgment is made for permission to quote from the following:

Curious Naturalists by Niko Tinbergen, Basic Books, Inc. Publishers, New York, 1958.
The Herring Gull's World by Niko Tinbergen, Basic Books, Inc. Publishers, New York, 1961.
King Solomon's Ring by Konrad Lorenz. Copyright 1952 by Thomas Y. Crowell Company, publishers, and reprinted with permission of Thomas Y. Crowell Company and Methuen & Co. Ltd., London.

To Our Friends and Collaborators

Monty
Honkey
Casey
Lonna
Jeff
Candy
Snowball
Sam
Rimpie
Mijnsje
Christopher
Barnaby
Pucci
Ricky
Jiminy
Missie
Fifi

Who Have the Right Instincts

Contents

Allan D. Cruickshank from National Audubon Society

A young cowbird being fed by its foster mother, a vireo. Cowbirds sometimes grow twice as big as their foster parents.

1.

What Is Instinct?

Watching and waiting, a cowbird lurks in the bushes near a song sparrow's nest. She waits until the sparrow flies off in search of food. Then she dashes into the nest, lays an egg, and quickly departs.

When the sparrow returns, she doesn't seem to notice the extra egg. She just settles down in her nest again as if nothing unusual has happened.

The cowbird, meanwhile, is already hunting for another nest. Every day or two, she deposits one of her speckled eggs in the nest of a robin, a vireo, a warbler, or some other small bird. She never builds a nest of her own and never comes back to see her offspring.

Before long, cowbirds begin to hatch in nests scattered through the fields and woods. Usually the foster parents accept the little stranger as one of their own. They spend all day gathering food and stuffing it into the gaping mouths of their own infants—and the gaping mouth of the little cowbird.

A cowbird often grows much faster than its nestmates. Sometimes it fills up the entire nest and smothers the other young birds. It may even grow twice as big as its foster parents. Nevertheless, they go right on stuffing food into its hungry mouth.

Fat and healthy, it finally leaves the nest and flies off to join a flock of other cowbirds in a nearby field or pasture. All of these cowbirds have emerged from nests belonging to birds of different species, but they do not imitate the adopted parents who fed and cared for them. From the beginning, they behave in typical cowbird fashion.

They follow herds of grazing cows, and as they run about the cows' feet, they catch insects stirred up by the herd. When the time comes for them to produce young of their own, the cycle begins again. Like their mothers before them, young females lay their eggs in other birds' nests, and a new generation of cowbirds is raised by a new generation of foster parents.

Every cowbird starts life in strange surroundings, isolated from others of its kind. When it leaves its foster home, however, it is already equipped with certain built-in patterns of behavior. The young bird inherits these behavior patterns from the parents it has never seen, just as it inherits its brown head and gray body. Its squeaky cowbird call, its lazy feeding habits, and its strange nesting behavior are all controlled by *instinct*—behavior that is inborn and does not have to be learned.

Built-in Behavior

Unlike the cowbird, most birds build nests and care for their own young. However, most reptiles, fish, insects, and other lower animals never see their young. The female simply lays her eggs and disappears, leaving her offspring to fend for themselves.

These young animals are on their own from the moment they hatch. If they are going to survive, they must be able to find food and avoid the many dangers awaiting them.

Guided by instinct, a newly hatched praying mantis catches its first insect with as much speed and skill as an experienced adult. A baby sea turtle crawls out of its nest in the sand and races straight down the beach to the open sea. And a pink salmon, scarcely out of the egg, sets out on one of nature's great adventures.

Pink salmon hatch in early spring from eggs buried deep beneath the gravel of cold, swift-running streams in Alaska and British Columbia. Soon after they emerge from the gravel, the tiny fingerlings head downstream to the Pacific, where they will spend most of their lives swimming in large schools hundreds of miles out at sea.

Feeding at first on microscopic sea creatures, and later on fish smaller than themselves, the salmon grow rapidly

Going home: salmon overcome staggering obstacles as they migrate back to their birthplace.

Fisheries Association of British Columbia

until they reach maturity about a year after they hatch. At this point, they leave their mid-ocean feeding grounds and begin a hazardous journey back to the place where they were born. Sweeping across the Pacific, they return to the coast and somehow find the mouth of their home river. Then they fight their way upstream, swimming against strong rapids, leaping over waterfalls, branching off into smaller rivers, streams and creeks. No one knows exactly how they find their way, yet with unerring accuracy they finally arrive at the spawning ground where they themselves were hatched.

The salmon are sleek and fat when they begin this journey. But they eat nothing along the way and when they reach their destination, they are ragged and emaciated. Their stomachs are shriveled and their skin is discolored by fungus. They have just enough strength left to mate and bury their eggs beneath the gravel. Shortly afterwards, they begin to die.

When the new generation hatches the following spring, not a single older salmon is still alive. Yet these infant fish embark on the same round-trip journey their parents completed the year before.

Even when an animal depends on its parents for food and protection, built-in patterns of behavior play an important role in its life. A herring gull chick, just hatched and lying helplessly in its nest, must beg for its first meal by pecking at a small red spot on its parent's bill. If it fails to perform this instinctive act, it will not be fed.

A newborn deer reacts automatically to danger by "freezing" motionless. No one teaches the fawn to behave like this, yet it "freezes" instantly at the slightest alarm.

Australian News and Information Bureau

Before it can complete its development, a baby kangaroo must find its way to a pouch on its mother's abdomen.

Camouflaged against the dappled light and shade of the underbrush by its spotted fur, it usually goes unnoticed.

Few baby animals are more helpless than a newborn kangaroo. Except for its mouth and its claw-tipped forefeet, a kangaroo's two-inch-long body is still unformed at birth. Before it can complete its development, it must find its way to a pouch on its mother's abdomen.

As a kangaroo emerges from the womb, its mother begins to lick her belly, creating a wet pathway through the fur. Using its claws, the infant crawls up the furry pathway, climbs into its mother's pouch, and attaches itself to a milk nipple. Instinct has equipped this blind little creature to perform the one act necessary for its survival.

Like One, Like All

On a beach in Oregon, a herring gull looks up from its nest and sounds a long, rhythmic alarm call: *gagaga! gagagagaga!* The call is taken up by other adults in the colony and they soar into the air, ready to attack any predator which threatens their young.

Six thousand miles away, on an island off the coast of Britain, another herring gull sounds the same alarm call: *gagaga! gagagagaga!* Echoing this call, adult birds fly up and prepare to attack.

This scene is repeated time and time again wherever herring gulls build their nests. Each gull inherits a built-in signal code from its ancestors; without having to learn, it utters and understands various calls expressing different states of feeling. If it had to *learn* these calls, as a child learns the words of human language, it is quite likely that herring gulls on the Pacific Coast would not "speak the same language" as their relatives in northern Europe.

Scientists use the term *species-typical behavior* to describe acts that seem to be innate, or inborn. An animal always performs these acts in the same way as every other member of its species. In fact, an animal can be identified by its species-typical behavior patterns just as surely as it can be identified by the physical characteristics of its body.

Dogs bury bones all over the world. Cats hiss at their enemies whether they live in Hollywood, Helsinki or Hong Kong. A trap-door spider in Arizona constructs the same kind of silk-lined burrow as a trap-door spider in Florida. Each species of bird sings its own typical song and builds its own typical nest.

An expert can recognize a canary or any other bird simply by listening to its song or by looking at its nest. Canaries have been hatched in incubators and raised in experimental laboratories where they never saw nests of any kind. When given the right materials, however, they always build typical canary nests the first time they try.

PROJECT
Observe the Hunting Skills of an Inexperienced Kitten

An adult cat is an expert hunter. When it attempts to capture a mouse, a bird, a fish, or some other prey, it performs a series of highly specialized movements which have enabled cats to survive and flourish for millions of years. The same movements are performed almost to perfection by an inexperienced kitten as it plays with a dangling string, a rubber ball, or some other toy. Even if the kitten has been raised indoors and has never seen a real mouse, bird or fish, it instinctively "knows" the hunting techniques typical of its species—techniques used by all cats everywhere.

1. Observe a kitten as it plays with a rubber ball. Note how the kitten "examines" the ball by reaching forward and touching it with a flexed paw. Then it crouches, glaring tensely at its plaything. At this point the kitten may perform a treading movement with its hind legs, as though it is seeking a firm foothold from which to spring. Suddenly it leaps forward and pounces on the ball with its forepaws held closely together. Caught up in this game, it may even bite the ball. These are the same movements an adult cat uses to capture its most important prey—the mouse.

2. A playing kitten will often cuff a ball with its paw. The ball may roll under a sofa or other piece of furniture which is too close to the floor for the kitten to crawl underneath. When

this happens, watch how the kitten reaches with one arm into the space and retrieves the ball just as a grown cat might thrust its paw into a mouse hole to retrieve an escaping prey.

3. If you attach a ball, a clump of feathers, or another suitable object to the end of a string and dangle it above the kitten's head, the kitten will change its "hunting" technique. Leaping into the air with arms outstretched and claws extended, it will try to grab the ball with both paws at once, by bringing them quickly together in a wide, sweeping movement. Adult cats use an identical grasping movement as they try to seize a bird which is just leaving the ground.

4. As you watch the kitten play, you will see it use other

species-typical hunting techniques. Occasionally it may reach under its plaything and with a quick upward motion, toss the toy into the air and over its shoulder. Following the flying object with its eyes, the kitten will pursue it with a high leap and a swift pounce. An adult cat uses the same skillful technique to scoop a fish out of a pond or stream.

5. Observe the play behavior of several kittens. Carefully list and describe the various movements and responses that the kittens seem to have in common. When you become familiar with some of the innate behavior patterns typical of cats, try to determine how each kind of behavior may have helped the cat family to survive.

The Wisdom and Ignorance of Instinct

A hunting wasp appears to be a conscientious mother. She certainly makes elaborate preparations for the safety and well-being of her future offspring.

To begin with, she digs a hole in the ground. Then she flies off in search of an insect—not just any insect, but one of the caterpillars her species has always hunted. When she finds one she stings it, paralyzing but not killing the creature, so it will be fresh and edible when her larva needs food.

The wasp hauls her victim along the ground, drags it into her burrow, and lays a single egg upon it. Then she covers up the nest, piles small pebbles around the entrance, and pounds the pebbles into place with her head. Finally, she grasps a loose pebble in her jaws and uses it as a tool to flatten down the soil. Her task completed, she flies away and starts work on another nest. The wasp will never return to watch her larva hatch and eat the paralyzed caterpillar.

A hunting wasp at the entrance to her burrow.

The behavior of the hunting wasp was first studied nearly a century ago by a French naturalist named Jean Henri Fabre. Fascinated by what he called "the wisdom of instinct," Fabre planned an experiment to see if a wasp understands what she is doing when she builds a nest, stocks it with provisions, and skillfully conceals the entrance.

One day Fabre interrupted a wasp as she was beginning to seal the door to her burrow. Pushing the insect aside, he carefully removed the paralyzed caterpillar from inside the nest with a pair of forceps. As he did so, he saw that the wasp's egg was still clinging to the caterpillar's breast.

"Having done this," Fabre wrote, "and put the caterpillar safely away in a box, I yield my place to the wasp, who has been on the watch beside me while I was rifling her home. Finding the door open, she goes in and stays for a few moments. Then she comes out and resumes her work where I interrupted it."

The wasp behaved as though nothing had happened. Though her burrow was now empty and useless, she continued to seal its entrance with sand and pebbles.

"When the door is thoroughly walled up," Fabre continues, "the insect brushes herself, seems to give a glance of satisfaction at the task completed, and finally flies away. ...Doesn't she realize that the cell is empty? I dare not accuse her of such stupidity. She is aware of it. Then why that other piece of stupidity which makes her close—and very conscientiously close—an empty burrow? Here the work of closing is useless, is supremely absurd. No matter: the insect performs this task with as much care as if the larva's future depended on it. . . .

"What object can the wasp have in blocking up a burrow which has become useless, now that it no longer contains the victim and the egg, and which will always remain useless, since the wasp will not return to it?"

Fabre called this "the ignorance of instinct." However far-sighted a wasp's behavior may seem, she is behaving quite automatically—like a machine that has been wound up and set in motion.

Animals appear to be acting with wisdom and foresight when they build nests, gather supplies of food, and care for their young. However, these acts are often automatic responses which require no thought or understanding. When an animal behaves instinctively, it does not necessarily know what it is doing or why.

Flies constantly preen their wings to keep them free of dust, yet a deformed fly, which has never grown wings, will go through all the typical motions of wing-preening. A cat will instinctively "sharpen its claws" on tree trunks, furniture, or other handy objects even if its claws were removed while it was still a kitten. A well-fed squirrel, raised from birth in captivity, will dig energetically at the wire floor of its cage, "bury" nuts in a "hole" that doesn't exist, then go away contented even though the nuts are still exposed to full view.

Instinct compels a mother robin to stuff food into the gaping mouths she sees in her nest. The mere sight of these mouths triggers the robin's food-stuffing response. She will feed a strange cowbird just as readily as her own young. She will even stuff worms into a wooden model that looks more or less like a gaping mouth. If this model is bigger than the gaping mouths of the robin's nestlings, she will automatically stuff all the food she gathers into the model and let her nestlings die of starvation.

At one time, the word "instinct" was applied freely to almost every kind of behavior that was not clearly understood. It was said that a squirrel buries nuts because of a "hoarding instinct," that a robin feeds her young because

Responding automatically to odor trails laid down by their leaders, blind army ants follow each other around a laboratory dish. Once started on this course, they will continue to march until they die.

Courtesy of The American Museum of Natural History

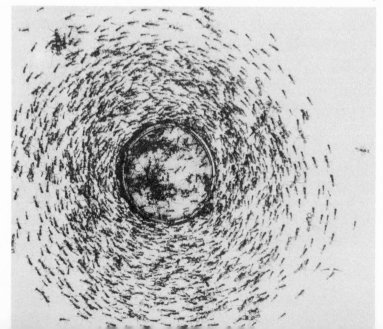

of a "maternal instinct," that a rabbit flees from danger because of a "survival instinct." Today, scientists are no longer satisfied to explain behavior in this way. The word "instinct" is still used to describe behavior that seems to emerge without learning in all members of a given species, but the word itself does not explain *why* an animal behaves as it does.

What makes an animal behave in a certain way at a certain time? How can an animal inherit complex patterns of behavior from its ancestors? To what extent is an animal's behavior affected by experience and learning?

Thousands of scientists, specializing in many different fields and working in countries throughout the world, are attempting to answer such questions. The study of animal behavior is called *ethology,* a word that only recently found its way into the dictionary, for this is still a young science. So far, we have barely started to penetrate the mysteries of animal life. But our knowledge is growing. As it does, it will pay rich dividends in our efforts to understand not only the living creatures who surround us, but also ourselves.

2.

Investigating Instinct

Does a young bird learn to fly?

It certainly *looks* as though a fledgling learns. Often, a young bird seems reluctant to test its wings and must be coaxed from the nest by its parents. They may call to it from the ground as it peeks cautiously over the side of its nest. Some parents make short "demonstration flights" in front of the nest. Others will push a fledgling out of its nest—forcing it to fly.

Suddenly, the little bird finds itself airborne. Flapping its wings, it circles in the air and heads for the nearest landing place. More "practice flights" follow as it flutters awkwardly from limb to limb, from its tree to the ground and back again. Gradually it seems to increase its skill, and before long it is flying as well as its parents.

We can learn a great deal about animals by watching them in their natural surroundings, yet our observations often raise questions which can be answered only through carefully planned experiments. Observation tells us that an inexperienced young bird makes many short, hesitant flights at first. Are these trial flights necessary? Must the fledgling practice before it develops the ability to fly perfectly?

With these questions in mind, a German scientist named Josef Grohmann planned an experiment with young pigeons.

Courtesy of The American Museum of Natural History

st-hand observation of animals in ir natural surroundings supplies ch of our knowledge about animal avior. Working at night in the l, these scientists are photograph- spring peepers and recording their nds.

Observations often raise questions which must be answered through carefully planned laboratory experiments. In his lab at The American Museum of Natural History, Dr. Helmut E. Adler studies the feeding responses of a starling.

Growing Up

Long before it leaves its nest, a young pigeon begins to flap its wings as though it is "flying in place." It appears to be practicing the movements of flying. Dr. Grohmann raised some newly hatched pigeons in narrow cardboard tubes, where they could not move their wings at all. Other pigeons, hatched at the same time, were raised by their parents under natural conditions. When these birds were old enough to leave their nests and fly a certain distance, Grohmann released the confined birds from their cardboard tubes. Without any chance to practice or learn, the "tube birds" were able to fly as far and as well as normal pigeons their own age.

This experiment demonstrated that an inexperienced bird automatically performs the complex movements necessary for flying. Ordinarily, a fledgling takes off on its first awkward flights before its wings and flying muscles are fully developed. Its flying ability improves not because of practice—but simply because it is growing older.

Because the bodies of many young animals are not fully developed at birth, they cannot perform at first all the acts which later will come naturally. Some inborn behavior patterns emerge gradually, as the body matures.

Even a child's ability to walk may depend mainly on his physical development, and not on learning. In the American Southwest, the Hopi and Navajo Indians traditionally kept their infants bound to boards carried on the mother's back. These cradleboards restrict the movements a growing baby can make with his arms and legs. Some Indian mothers have continued to follow this custom, while others have not. Yet babies strapped to cradleboards for most of the day begin to walk at about the same time as those who are allowed to move about freely.

As the body develops and grows, changes in physical appearance may occur. Male and female chicks look just

*U.S. Bureau
of Indian Affairs*

Navajo mother and child: a cradleboard restricts a baby's movements but does not affect his ability to crawl or walk.

Lion and lioness.

alike, but when they grow up the rooster acquires a large, brightly colored comb which distinguishes him from a hen; he also develops a bigger body and longer tail feathers. A mature lion possesses an impressive mane, setting him apart from a lioness. A full-grown stag has antlers, which a doe lacks. In the same way, the bodies of boys and girls change into those of men and women.

These physical changes are brought about by certain *hormones*—chemical substances released into the bloodstream by special glands. Scientists have identified various kinds of hormones which affect the body in many ways. The word "hormone," in fact, comes from a Greek word meaning "to stimulate."

Some hormones are present in the body at birth; among other things, they regulate growth and development. The sex hormones, however, do not appear until the body begins to mature. Released by the reproductive glands—the *ovaries* in the female and the *testes* in the male—sex hormones affect the body's outward appearance and also stimulate new kinds of behavior.

The Chemistry of Behavior

When sex hormones begin to appear in a growing animal's body, the animal displays for the first time an interest in courtship, nest-building, and mating. It is possible to demonstrate the effects of these hormones by injecting them directly into an animal's bloodstream. If a baby chick is injected with male sex hormones, he starts to crow like a rooster and struts boldly about the barnyard in typical rooster fashion. A female chick begins to act like a full-grown hen when she is injected with female sex hormones. Experiments have shown that hormone injections can make many immature animals behave just like adults.

Scientists have known for some time that hormones affect behavior. But it is only now becoming clear that behavior, in turn, can stimulate the flow of hormones inside an animal's body.

At Rutgers University in New Jersey, Dr. Daniel S. Lehrman has investigated some of the complex relationships between hormones and behavior. Dr. Lehrman works mainly with the ring dove, a small relative of the domestic pigeon. These birds, like most others, breed only at a certain time of the year. During the winter their reproductive glands are inactive. In spring, stimulated by the change of seasons and other factors, their glands begin to release sex hormones which bring the birds into breeding condition.

When ring doves are ready to mate, they always behave

in a certain way—in a manner typical of their species. The male struts about, his head held high. Then he approaches the female, bows before her, and coos. The female watches this courtship display with apparent interest, and after a while the birds begin to build their nest.

This job continues for a week or longer as the male gathers nesting material and delivers it to his mate, who does the actual nest weaving. When the nest is finished, the female lays two eggs and both birds take turns sitting on them until they hatch.

What causes this behavior? Do the doves sit simply because they can see two eggs in their nest?

In one of his early experiments at Rutgers, Dr. Lehrman placed a male and female in a cage and immediately gave them a ready-made nest containing two dove eggs. Both birds were in breeding condition, yet they acted as if the nest and eggs didn't exist. Instead of sitting on the planted eggs, the doves performed their typical courtship ceremony: the male strutted, bowed, and cooed before the female.

Then they started to build a new nest on top of the one that had been placed in their cage. Dr. Lehrman had to remove the eggs from the planted nest to keep them from breaking. After the doves had completed their own nest, the scientist placed the strange eggs inside it, and the doves sat on them immediately.

By conducting many similar experiments, Lehrman established an important fact about the doves' breeding behavior. These birds always perform a series of acts one after the other. When two doves meet for the first time, they are interested only in courtship. Then they become

Scientific American

Breeding behavior of ring doves begins soon after a male and a female meet for the first time. . . .

The male bows and coos before the female. . . .

interested in nestbuilding. And after they have built a nest, they are ready to sit on eggs.

Would it be possible to change the doves' behavior by tampering with their body chemistry? Dr. Lehrman injected a male and female with sex hormones, placed the birds in a cage, and gave them another ready-made nest containing two eggs. The extra dose of hormones had a dramatic effect: the doves sat on the strange eggs right away—without taking time to perform their courtship ceremony or to build their own nest.

How can hormone injections take the place of such activities as courtship and nestbuilding? "A good experiment," says Dr. Lehrman, "always raises more questions than it answers."

Once again, the scientist placed a male and a female in a cage, but now the birds were separated by a glass plate. As the male looked at the female through the glass, he began to strut, bow, and coo. The female watched, and in the next week, she laid two eggs. When Dr. Lehrman ex-

Next the birds cooperate in nest-building. . . .

After that they are ready to sit on eggs.

amined this female, he found that her ovaries had grown several times larger.

Had the mere sight of a male through a plate glass window caused this change to occur in the female's body? The same experiment was now repeated with two other birds. This time, however, the male's reproductive glands had been removed. As a result of this operation, he did not strut about, bow, or coo like a normal male. Instead, he paid no attention to the female on the other side of the glass plate. This female laid no eggs. Unlike the female in the previous experiment, her ovaries did not grow larger.

A female dove is affected not simply by the sight of a male—but by a male who struts, bows, and coos. This "male behavior" brings about an extra flow of hormones in the female's body, causing her ovaries to grow larger and stimulating her to build a nest and lay eggs. Contact with the nest increases the flow of hormones even more, preparing the female to sit on her eggs until they hatch.

Courtship and nestbuilding, Dr. Lehrman found, also increase the flow of hormones in the body of the male dove—preparing him to play his role as a father.

Keys That Unlock Behavior

Prowling through the forest, a hungry wolf stops short and sniffs the ground. A moment later, he sets out on the scent trail of a rabbit.

The wolf is reacting to a powerful *stimulus*—a condition in the environment that causes an animal to respond. A stimulus can be anything an animal senses in its surroundings, or it can be a change taking place inside the animal's body.

An internal stimulus—such as hunger, thirst, or the production of hormones—prepares an animal to behave in a certain way. An external stimulus—something the animal smells, sees, hears, feels, or tastes—triggers the appropriate kind of behavior. The scent of a rabbit triggers the hunting behavior of a hungry wolf. The sight of a strutting, bowing male triggers the mating behavior of a female dove. These external stimuli have been called "keys that unlock behavior."

A key that unlocks the maternal behavior of a turkey hen is the sound of her chicks' peeping. The turkey doesn't recognize her chicks by sight. If she is given a toy which peeps like a chick, she will accept it as her own. If anything approaches her nest which doesn't peep like a chick, she will attempt to kill it. If for some reason the turkey cannot hear, she will kill her own chicks.

Every form of behavior is a reaction to a stimulus of some kind. When a mouse hears the high-pitched distress call of her young, she reacts by rushing to their rescue. A fish sees a worm squirming on a hook and reacts by strik-

Responding to a stimulus.

ing. A spider feels its web vibrate and crawls out to devour a struggling fly.

A female tick sometimes spends most of her life waiting for the right stimulus to come along. These wingless, blood-sucking insects burrow into the skin of humans, cattle, sheep and other mammals. After mating, a female will climb slowly to the outermost tip of a high bush and will cling there until a mammal passes beneath her. She may stay on the bush for weeks or months, without responding to the hundreds of sounds, smells, and other changes taking place around her. She waits until one particular stimulus acts as a signal for her to release her grip. This stimulus is the smell of butyric acid—a chemical produced by the skin glands of man and other mammals.

Often, an animal responds not to a single smell, sight, sound, taste, or sensation, but to a combination of stimuli which may be difficult to identify. Dr. Niko Tinbergen, a native of Holland who now teaches at England's Oxford University, is famous for his detective work in this field. In one series of experiments, he investigated keys that unlock the mating behavior of a grayling butterfly.

When a male grayling is ready to mate, he waits on a tree trunk until a female flutters by. Then he flies off in pursuit. Strangely enough, a male in a mating mood may also pursue other kinds of insects, small songbirds, falling leaves, and even his own shadow. What exactly is the butterfly reacting to?

Dr. Tinbergen and his associates went out into grayling butterfly country, carrying with them paper models in a variety of sizes, colors, and shapes. Some of these models looked like real butterflies. Others were shaped like circles, rectangles, and squares. One by one, the models were tied to fishing rods and were dangled before every male grayling the scientists could find.

"The males responded readily to these models," wrote Dr. Tinbergen, "and thus began a study which kept us busy—and our friends amused—through several seasons. The three or four of us would continually patrol miles of grayling country and present our models to every male we found. . . .

"We presented a remarkable spectacle in our practical but scarcely attractive field dress of shorts, broad-brimmed straw hats and sun glasses, each of us with his two rods, all with dangling paper models, trying not to get them entangled in bushes or heather, staring intently after one of our graylings, trying to follow it on its erratic flight, running after it, suddenly stopping, stalking it, then carefully going through our angling ritual repeated three times, and finally making a few notes; all this with tense, serious faces. No wonder we drew curious and suspicious glances from the occasional passerby who happened to see us at work."

Altogether, the scientists performed some 50,000 tests. They found that the shape of their paper models made little difference. A male grayling will fly off in pursuit of a circle or square just as readily as he will pursue a model shaped like a real butterfly.

Color did make a difference, however, for the males seemed to prefer darker shades. They chased black models even more readily than the natural brown of the grayling female. White models were the least effective.

Larger models worked better than smaller ones. In fact, a model four times the size of an average female was more popular among the males than a normal-sized model.

But the most important factor, as it turned out, was the way a model moved through the air. If the scientists jiggled their poles so that a model fluttered and danced as a female does, the model attracted many more males than one which glided smoothly through the air.

These experiments explained why a male grayling will sometimes pursue other kinds of insects, small birds, or its own shadow. The male does not actually recognize a grayling female as such. The key that unlocks his mating behavior is a dark object of a certain size that *dances* through the air. A male will pursue any such object, whatever it may be.

Occasionally, scientists "improve" on nature by offering an animal an artificial stimulus which is more effective than a real one. As Dr. Tinbergen found, a male

Supernormal stimulus: in an experiment conducted by Dutch scientists, a herring gull ignores a normal-size egg and tries to incubate a giant egg.

grayling will ignore a real female in favor of an extra-large paper model. In another series of experiments, Tinbergen discovered that a herring gull is more attracted to a super-large artificial egg than to one of normal size. If a gull is given the choice between a real egg and a wooden replica twenty times as large, it will attempt to sit on the giant egg, even though it keeps falling off. Such an egg is called a *supernormal stimulus.*

How Behavior Develops

Soon after hatching, a chick struggles to its feet and starts to walk. By the time it is a day old, it is already running around the barnyard, scratching and pecking for food. At first glance, this automatic pecking response seems to require no experience or learning. But if we look more closely, we begin to discover some of the factors that may affect the chick's feeding behavior.

By cutting a little window in the shell of an incubating egg, we can watch the chick embryo developing inside. The embryo is curled up in such a way that its head is resting on its breast. As the embryo's heart beats, its head and neck move up and down in rhythm with its beating heart. Some scientists believe that this is how the chick's pecking response first develops. If so, then we might say that the heart teaches the head to peck.

After the chick hatches, it begins to peck at objects on the ground. At first it misses many of the things it pecks at. But before long, its aim improves and it strikes its target almost every time. This improvement seems to result from the continuing development of the chick's body. As it grows, its muscles strengthen, it gets steadier on its feet, and perhaps its eyesight improves.

Meanwhile, another change occurs. Right after hatching, the chick pecks at any small round object it happens to see—grains of food, small pebbles, marks on the ground, and sometimes its own feet. Gradually it becomes more selective. It learns to ignore objects it cannot eat and to peck only at grains of real food. Thus, the chick's pecking response seems to be affected by conditions inside the egg, by its physical growth, and by its ability to learn.

Nearly all animals can learn, but some are able to learn a great deal more than others. Insects and other lower animals have only limited learning ability; their behavior is controlled almost entirely by instinct. But as we ascend the evolutionary scale from fish to amphibians, reptiles and birds, we find that animals have an increasingly larger part of their brain set aside for learning. By the time we reach mammals, the group that includes man, it becomes more and more difficult to determine what is innate and what is learned, for in these higher animals, experience constantly affects behavior.

As a result, scientists no longer classify behavior as purely instinctive or purely learned. On the contrary, heredity and experience both play a part in shaping a young animal's behavior.

It was once thought, for example, that a young animal's fear of high places was purely instinctive. Many young animals display extreme caution the first time they are exposed to a dangerous height. If a kitten is placed on a window ledge, it clings desperately with its claws and tries to back away—even though it has never been on a high place before. Recent experiments have shown, however, that an animal's fear of height is affected by its earliest experiences.

At Cornell University, kittens were raised from birth in an experimenal laboratory. When they were old enough to crawl about on their own, some of the kittens were placed in little carts. Others were outfitted with harnesses which were attached to the carts. Wherever these kittens went, they pulled their brothers and sisters along behind them. In this way, all the kittens covered the same ground and saw the same things. The important difference was that some moved under their own power, while others received a free ride and had no chance to move on their own.

PROJECT
Test Young Animals on a Visual Cliff

Many young animals have a built-in fear of heights. If a puppy or kitten is placed on a high ledge, for example, it will peer over the edge, bob its head up and down, and cautiously back away. It will behave like this even if it has never been on a high place before. By constructing a "visual cliff" similar to those used by scientists, you can test a variety of young animals for their ability to perceive and avoid dangerous heights.

1. Place a piece of clean glass or Plexiglas over the space between two tables, as shown below.

2. Lay a wooden plank across the glass so that one edge of

the plank lies directly above the edge of one table. This plank will serve as a runway on which you can place the animal you wish to test. To descend from the runway, an animal must choose between the "shallow side," where the glass covers the top of the table, and the "deep side," where the glass extends over the space between the tables.

3. Place a bright light under one table, as shown, so that the glass does not reflect the image of the animal you are testing.

4. The surface beneath the glass on both the shallow and deep sides must have the same appearance. A patterned material, such as a checkered tablecloth, can be used to cover both surfaces. The checks on the shallow side will appear larger because they are closer to the animal being tested. This will help the animal perceive the difference in depth on either side of the runway.

5. Kittens, puppies, newly hatched chicks, baby turtles, and many other animals can be tested on a visual cliff. Be sure that the animal you test has had no previous experience with heights. The best time to conduct your experiment is when the young animal first begins to move about and explore its surroundings on its own. Puppies and kittens begin to explore on their own when they are about four weeks old. You should carry the animal you are testing to the visual cliff in a closed box, so it does not have its first experience with height while being taken to the test site.

6. Allow the animal to leave the box and crawl onto the runway. How does the animal respond as it peers over each side of the runway? Does it descend from the runway on the shallow side, or the deep side?

7. Try to coax the animal to descend on the deep side. How does it react? What happens if you push the animal onto the glass over the deep side?

From the time they were born, all these kittens were exposed only to flat, level surfaces. Finally, they were tested for their ability to recognize heights. Kittens who had been allowed to move about under their own power displayed immediate fear when placed at the brink of a special laboratory "cliff." They froze motionless, extended their claws, and then backed up. Kittens who had been pulled about in carts, and had never moved on their own, behaved differently. They did not seem to recognize dangerous heights. When they approached the edge of the laboratory cliff, they showed no fear and failed to back away.

Exposed to height for the first time in its life, a Siamese kitten peers cautiously over the edge of a "visual cliff" during an experiment at Cornell University. The kitten is protected by a sheet of plate glass which covers the "chasm" below. Yet it will not step over the cliff even though it can feel the solid glass with its paw.

William Vandivert

Like other young mammals, a kitten seems to have an inborn fear of height—a fear that can save its life. Yet this "instinct" cannot develop unless the kitten has a chance to move about on its own as soon as it is able.

In many cases, an animal inherits the outline of a behavior pattern while the details are filled in by learning. A bird sings the typical song of its species, for instance, but in some cases, it must learn the details of that song. If a yellow bunting is raised in isolation, apart from others of its kind, the song it sings will be unnaturally simple and primitive. Before it can sing properly, it must listen to other yellow buntings. This bird inherits a basic song pattern from its ancestors, but the complete song must be learned anew in each generation.

Even a bird's flying ability depends partly on learning. As we have seen, a young bird can fly perfectly as soon as its wings and muscles are adequately developed. However, it cannot land perfectly. At first, it may lose its balance as it alights on a branch, or it may tumble over as it lands on the ground. Though its flying movements are directed by instinct, the young bird must master the same lesson every airplane pilot learns: it must learn from experience to come in for a landing against the wind.

3.

The Mystery of Migration

Somewhere in Canada, a monarch butterfly flutters into the air and heads south—bound for a distant place it has never seen. Flying alone over mountains, plains, and cities, tossed by winds and battered by rain, resting at night on trees or shrubs, this frail insect will wing its way a thousand miles or more. Somehow, it will find one of the few spots on the California coast where monarchs gather to spend the winter.

Billions of living creatures set out on migratory journeys every year. Flying, swimming, crawling, and walking, traveling by day or by night, in large groups or by themselves, crossing thousands of miles or a few hundred yards, the migrants press on toward destinations which have lured their ancestors for countless generations. Many are inexperienced young animals, migrating for the first time without guidance from their elders. Yet they perform feats of navigation far beyond the ability of any human.

What makes an animal migrate? How does it know when to leave, where to go, and how to get there?

Incredible Journeys

Of all animals, birds are the most dramatic migrants and

U.S. Bureau of Sport Fisheries and Wildlife

(*left*) At a Maryland game refuge, wildlife agents use nets to capture migrating waterfowl for banding. (*right*) A band is attached to the leg of a duck. Each band carries a serial number and the U.S. Fish and Wildlife Service address to which the band should be mailed. More than a million birds are banded every year.

the ones who have received the most scientific attention. As autumn begins, many familiar birds disappear from their northern homes. When spring arrives, they suddenly reappear. Men have always been fascinated by these seasonal comings and goings, but until the end of the last century, no one really knew where birds spend the long winter months.

The first effective method of tracking birds was introduced by Christian Mortensen, a Danish schoolmaster. In the summer of 1891 he captured some starlings in his garden and slipped metal identification bands around their legs. Then he released the birds, hoping that some of the bands would later be recovered and returned to him.

Mortensen's system of bird-banding was soon adopted throughout the world, and today, more than a million birds are banded every year. Each band carries an identification number and a return address. About one in ten banded birds is found again—sometimes thousands of miles away.

Recently, scientists have tried out new methods of charting migratory routes. Birds have been sprayed with brightly colored dyes. Tiny radio transmitters have been attached to their bodies. They have been tracked with radar and trailed in small airplanes. Similar methods are now being used to track migrating fish, turtles, bats, whales, bears, and other animals.

About a third of all the world's species of birds migrate during the course of the year. In North America and Eu-

(*left*) On the arctic icecap north of Point Barrow, Alaska, Dr. Vagn Flyger marks a polar bear with a long-lasting dye. Scientists immobilized the bear by shooting it with a syringe filled with a harmless drug which wears off in about 30 minutes. (*right*) Recovering from the effects of the drug, the bear gets up and continues on its way. The dyed spot will help identify the bear if it is sighted again, enabling scientists to map the animal's migration route.

Dr. Martin W. Schein, West Virginia University

rope, a majority of birds migrate. Some travel only a short distance, from high mountains down to sheltered valleys, or from inland areas to warmer coastal regions. Others escape the cold northern winter completely by flying thousands of miles across the equator to South America or Africa.

Barn swallows spend the spring and summer throughout much of the United States and Canada. Then they take off for various parts of South America. European swallows range from Scandinavia in the north all the way to South Africa.

The record for long-distance migration, however, is held by the arctic tern, a relative of the common sea gull. Each year, arctic terns span the globe from pole to pole. They nest along the ice-free coasts of the Arctic Ocean during the brief northern summer. When summer ends, they fly south to the fringes of the antarctic—a one-way journey of 10,000 miles or more.

Another shore bird, the American golden plover, migrates each year from arctic Canada to the grasslands of Argentina. Adult plovers leave their young behind when they set out on this journey. They fly eastward across Canada to the Atlantic; then they turn south and travel over the open sea until they reach South America.

Deserted by their parents, the young plovers begin their first migration entirely on their own. They even follow a different route, staying over land all the way. The young birds fly south across Canada, the United States, Mexico, and Central America, and then head directly for the Argentine grasslands. Guided by an inborn sense of direction scientists only dimly understand, they find their

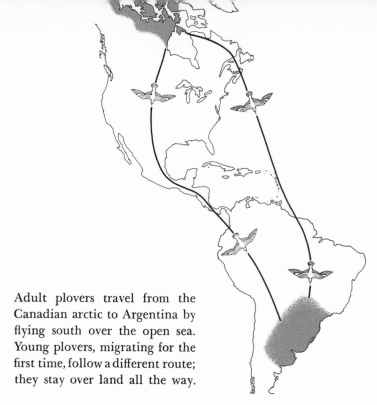

Adult plovers travel from the Canadian arctic to Argentina by flying south over the open sea. Young plovers, migrating for the first time, follow a different route; they stay over land all the way.

way from the arctic regions where they were born to their winter range 8000 miles away.

Migratory journeys are undertaken by a wide variety of animals. Bluefin tuna sweep northward during the spring from the sub-tropical waters of the Caribbean to feeding grounds off the coasts of Newfoundland and Nova Scotia. Gray whales leave their warm, sheltered lagoons along the coast of Mexico and head for the Arctic Ocean, where they feed on abundant supplies of plankton. North American caribou emerge from the forests and trudge through melting snows to grazing grounds far beyond the timber line in the Canadian tundra. Bats desert their winter caves and fly to summer quarters 150 or 200 miles away.

A green sea turtle begins its first migratory journey within minutes after hatching. Many of these reptiles

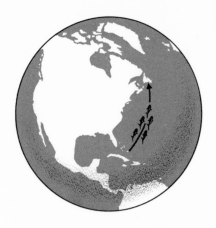

Arctic terns span the globe twice each year, traveling back and forth from the ice-free coasts of the arctic to the fringes of the antarctic.

Bluefin tuna migrate northward from spawning grounds in the Caribbean to summer feeding grounds off the coasts of New-foundland and Nova Scotia. Their return route to the Caribbean is unknown.

hatch from eggs buried deep in the sandy beaches of Ascension Island in the South Atlantic. The baby turtles dig their way up to the surface, race across the beach, and disappear into the sea. Carried by ocean currents, they eventually reach the coast of Brazil.

Every two or three years, mature turtles weighing 300 pounds or more make a return journey to their birthplace. Ascension Island is so small and remote, World War II pilots had trouble finding the place. But the turtles experience no such difficulty. Using only their animal senses as instruments of navigation, they manage to maintain a true course across 1400 miles of open sea. After mating in the warm waters around the island, the females climb ashore and bury their eggs. Leaving the eggs to

Monarch butterflies hatch in late summer throughout much of southern Canada and northern areas of the United States. As autumn approaches, they migrate south to winter quarters along the Gulf of Mexico and the California coast.

Gray whales spend the winter along the coast of Mexico and the summer feeding on plankton in the Arctic Ocean.

hatch unaided, they return to the sea and swim all the way back to Brazil.

The most spectacular insect migrant is the black-and-orange monarch butterfly. Every autumn, millions of these insects stream south from Canada and northern areas of the United States. Scientists have traced their migration routes by pasting identification tags on the butterflies' wings. Monarchs which hatch east of the Rocky Mountains fly to Florida, Texas, and Mexico for the winter. Western monarchs winter at a few select spots along the California coast.

Pacific Grove, California, is especially well known for its wintering butterflies. The insects descend on this sunny coastal town every October, after flying from Oregon, Washington, and British Columbia. When they reach Pacific Grove, they cluster by tens of thousands on pine, cypress, and eucalyptus trees. A hundred monarchs weigh scarcely more than an air-mail letter; yet they mass together in such vast numbers that sturdy branches bend beneath their weight. Monarchs are so highly valued in Pacific Grove, they are protected by a special law. City Ordinance No. 352 makes it "illegal to molest or interfere in any way with the peaceful occupancy of Monarch butterflies on their annual visit to the city."

When spring arrives, the butterflies leave Pacific Grove and head north again. No monarch lives long enough to make this journey more than once. Faded with age, their wings battered and torn, the insects die during the summer, after laying their eggs on the downy leaves of milkweed plants.

Within a few weeks, a new generation comes into the

Early arrivals: having migrated south from Oregon, Washington, and British Columbia, monarch butterflies cluster on a pine tree in Pacific Grove, California, where they will spend the winter.

Pacific Grove Chamber of Commerce

world, and that autumn, the cycle begins again. The young butterflies fly south to the same wintering sites, and even the same trees, that attracted their parents the autumn before.

PROJECT
Tagging Monarchs

Every year, throughout much of North America, young researchers participate in the wide-ranging butterfly-tagging project conducted by Dr. Fred Urquhart of the University of Toronto in Canada. Dr. Urquhart has investigated insect migrations for more than thirty years and is the author of a book titled *The Monarch Butterfly*. Research associates who work with him are responsible for rearing and tagging monarchs and other butterflies, and for reporting their activities to Dr. Urquhart's project headquarters in Toronto.

Alice Hopf

For a registration fee of $5.00, you can enroll as a research associate. You will receive as many tags as you need, instructions for applying the tags to butterflies, and a newsletter which keeps members up to date on the results of the tagging program. If you would like to take part in this project, you can obtain further information by writing to Dr. Fred Urquhart, Monarch Butterfly Research Project, Scarborough College, University of Toronto, West Hill, Ontario, Canada.

An Irresistible Urge

The swallows of San Juan Capistrano in California are famous for their punctual habits. Records kept for nearly two centuries show that they usually leave Capistrano for South America during the same week in October, and usually return during the same week in March.

Migrating birds often follow amazingly precise time-tables, their arrivals and departures governed more by the calendar date than by local weather conditions. Even if a bird has been hatched in an incubator and raised in a laboratory cage, it becomes unusually active as its migration season approaches. Flitting nervously about its cage and fluttering against the bars, the bird displays "migration restlessness."

How does a bird know when to migrate? One of the first scientists to investigate this question was Dr. William Rowan, a biologist at Canada's University of Alberta. Most birds in this area escape the severe Canadian winter by migrating south, yet they usually take off long before the weather turns cold. Rowan suspected that bird migration in his part of the world is stimulated not so much by changing temperatures—but by changes in the length of day. When Canadian birds fly south during the early autumn, the days are growing shorter. When they return north the following spring, the days are growing longer.

One summer, Rowan captured some crows and put them in a large outdoor cage. Normally, these birds leave Alberta in September and fly south to Oklahoma. This particular September, however, the captive crows were confronted with a seasonal switch.

How does a bird know when it is time to migrate?

Every evening, just before sunset, Rowan turned large electric spotlights on the crows' cage. Each day he left the lights on five minutes longer. Winter was on the way, but from the crows' point of view, the days were getting longer instead of shorter.

In the middle of November, Rowan examined the birds. He found that their reproductive glands had grown much larger—a change that normally takes place only in the spring. Increasing periods of "daylight" had brought the crows into breeding condition at the wrong time of year.

At this point, the scientist wanted to see what would happen if he set the crows free. Had they been completely fooled by the electric spotlights? Would they actually begin their "spring" migration and fly north?

The birds were released on a Thanksgiving weekend. By then, all other crows from the area had long since flown south to Oklahoma. Many of Dr. Rowan's crows flew north into the frozen Canadian wilderness. They went in the same direction they would normally follow during their springtime migration.

Rowan's pioneering experiments demonstrated that light can affect the state of a bird's body and also its behavior. Since then, scientists have found out how this happens. In spring, increasing periods of daylight stimulate a small gland, called the *pituitary gland,* at the base of a bird's brain. This "master gland" releases hormones which flow through the blood and activate the bird's reproductive glands, causing eggs to ripen in females and sperm to be formed in males. In the tropics, where days are about the same length all year long, the same process can be triggered by the onset of the rainy season.

Migratory birds become increasingly restless as these chemical changes take place in their bodies. Before long, they fly to their breeding grounds, were they find mates, build nests, and raise a new generation.

Scientists have found that they can bring a bird into breeding condition by injecting reproductive hormones directly into its bloodstream. When this happens, the bird may attempt to migrate no matter what time of year it is.

Hormones play a vital role in the travels of a wide range of animals. An animal does not think to itself, "Spring is here. It's time to get moving." On the contrary, the animal feels an irresistible urge to migrate because of glandular secretions which operate in tune with the seasons.

Finding the Way

Each spring, American robins return to their nesting

grounds with the accuracy of guided missiles. Studies show that three out of every four robins build nests within a five-mile radius of their nesting sites the year before. Some of these birds return to the same field or garden year after year.

In the antarctic one summer, scientists invaded a colony of Adélie penguins, banded some of the birds for future identification, and marked the positions of their nests. A few weeks later, the penguins migrated hundreds of miles northward to their winter feeding grounds at the outer edge of the antarctic ice pack. The following spring, as the ice began to break up and melt, they set out on their return journey.

Walking single-file across the ice, sliding long distances on their bellies, swimming through open stretches of water, and hitching rides on moving ice floes, the flightless birds made their way across the white, empty landscape. Finally, they reached their summer nesting grounds on the rocky shore of the antarctic continent. Al-

Adélie penguins at their summer nesting grounds on the shore of Cape Crozier, Antarctica.

Michael C. T. Smith from National Audubon Society

though snow still covered the region, the penguins gathered stones along the beach and built their nests—piling the stones on top of the snow. Soon, the snow began to melt. As the stones sank through the slush, they settled on top of the old nests the penguins had built the summer before.

The direction-finding ability of birds is not limited to seasonal migrations. For centuries, homing pigeons have carried messages in small capsules attached to their legs. A young pigeon learns during training flights to recognize the area around its home loft. Afterwards, it can be placed in a sealed box and taken hundreds of miles away to an area it has never seen. When released, it will circle in the air and will then head directly for its home loft.

Impressive feats of navigation have been achieved by many kinds of birds. A few years ago, a Manx shearwater was taken from its nest on a small island off the coast of Britain. The bird was placed in a box and was transported by plane 3000 miles away to the Boston airport. Then it was released. Twelve days later, it showed up at its home nest. The bird had flown back across the Atlantic at an average speed of 250 miles a day.

Similar experiments have been conducted with a number of other animals. In a Florida cypress swamp, an alligator was sealed in a box and was taken 20 miles away before being set loose. Eventually, the big reptile made its way back to its home den. Compared with long distance homing of pigeons, this may not seem very impressive, but for a lumbering creature which normally stays within a half-mile of its den, it is a remarkable performance. Dogs and cats have been known to find their way home from unfamiliar places 25 miles away and more. Bats have returned to their home cave after being transported 150 miles away.

How does an animal find its way across unfamiliar territory? For years, scientists were baffled by this question. A major breakthrough occurred during the 1950's when a young German scientist named Gustav Kramer carried out a brilliant series of experiments with starlings. The birds were taken from their nests soon after hatching and were raised in a large outdoor aviary. When it was time for them to migrate, they became increasingly restless. Dr. Kramer wanted to see if the starlings would attempt to fly in the correct migratory direction, and if so, what clues they used to determine that direction.

For the purposes of these experiments, the birds were moved from their aviary to a specially designed outdoor cage. The cage had a Plexiglas floor. Kramer was able to lie on his back beneath the floor and keep track of the birds' movements.

To begin with, he studied the movements of one starling. This bird displayed all the typical symptoms of migration restlessness. It fluttered constantly over its perch, as though it were "flying in place," and it made many trips from the center of the cage to the edges and back again.

Kramer found that the bird tended to fly toward the northeast—the same compass direction it would follow at that time of year if it were free to migrate. The scientist tried to confuse the starling. He kept turning the cage around, he moved it from one location to another, and he placed a screen around the cage so the bird could not see any surrounding landmarks. None of this made any difference. The starling still attempted to fly toward the northeast.

As long as the bird could see the blue sky above, it always chose the correct migratory direction. But if the sky was overcast, the starling seemed to lose its sense of direction. Apparently, the bird was orienting itself by the sun!

Kramer decided to see if he could fool the bird by "moving" the sun. Outside the cage he set up screens which hid the sun's actual position in the sky. Then he installed adjustable mirrors which reflected the sun's rays. From inside the cage, it appeared as if the sun's position had changed. The starling immediately changed the direction in which it attempted to fly, according to the "new" position of the sun.

Kramer's mirror trick suggested that the bird was able to strike out in a certain direction by noting the sun's position in the sky. In further experiments, the scientist found that a starling can make allowance for the sun's daily movement across the sky as it rises in the east and sets in the west. If the bird wants to fly south, for example, it must keep the sun over its left wing in the morning, directly ahead at noon, and over its right wing in the afternoon.

This seemed such an incredible achievement for a bird, some scientists refused to accept the results of Kramer's experiments. Yet additional experiments since then have left little doubt that starlings and other birds are capable of what is now called *sun-compass orientation*. These birds not only navigate by the sun, but also compensate for its apparent movement across the sky during the course of a day.

Many birds migrate at night. Another German scientist, Dr. Franz Sauer, suspected that these birds might navigate by the stars. He began to experiment with warblers, small songbirds which travel from Europe to Africa every autumn.

"Some of them migrate as far as from Scandinavia to the southern part of Africa—a distance of thousands of miles," Dr. Sauer wrote. "Most remarkable of all is that each bird finds its own way to its destination! The warblers do not follow a leader or make the journey as a group; they navigate individually. And young birds making their first migration reach their goal just as surely as the experienced travelers. Somehow, purely by instinct, the warblers know exactly how to set their course. Since they fly only at night, we are impelled to ask: Do the warblers navigate by the stars?"

Sauer worked with warblers which had been hatched in incubators and raised inside his laboratory. These birds knew nothing of the outside world. They saw the sky for the first time in their lives when the scientist placed them in an outdoor cage with a glass top.

Despite their lack of experience, the warblers exhibited migration restlessness at the right time of year. As long as they could see the starry sky above their cage, they attempted to fly south—in the direction of Africa. But if the stars were hidden by clouds, the birds lost their sense of direction and flew aimlessly about.

"To adopt a definite direction," wrote Sauer, "they

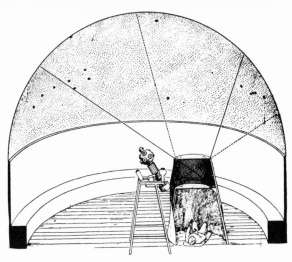

In Planetarium Experiment, birds display star-compass orientation when tested in cage placed under a dome showing replica of the sky.

needed a look at the starry sky. Indeed, the birds watched the sky so intently, meteors made them change their direction momentarily."

The scientist decided to continue his experiments in a nearby planetarium, which had a curved dome showing an artificial replica of the natural sky. The warblers' cage was placed on a stand near the floor of the planetarium, so the birds could see the curved dome 20 feet above. Sauer lay on his back beneath the cage, where he was able to watch the birds' movements.

If the dome was illuminated only with a soft light showing no stars, the warblers were unable to choose a definite direction. But if the planetarium sky matched the night sky over Germany at that time of year, the birds attempted to fly toward Africa—just as though they were seeing the natural sky.

By shifting the artificial stars and constellations about, Sauer could show his warblers the night sky as it then appeared at various points between Germany and Africa. In this way, it was possible to "guide" the birds. Whenever the stars shifted, the warblers changed direction accordingly, so that they were always heading toward "Africa." Though they had spent their entire lives in a cage, and had never traveled anywhere, they were capable of *star-compass orientation*.

"At their very first glimpse of the sky," wrote Sauer, "the birds automatically know the right direction. Without benefit of previous experience, with no cue except the stars, the birds are able to locate themselves in time and space and find the way to their destined homes."

It is not yet clear just how birds use the stars to navigate. They may be guided by prominent constellations or by certain individual stars, such as the North Star. However, since the stars move across the sky at night, just as the sun moves during the day, night migrants must make allowance for the constantly changing positions of the stars.

These discoveries about birds led to similar experiments with other animals. It now appears that certain fish, reptiles, insects, and even crabs can also navigate by the sun or stars. At present, this direction-finding ability is only vaguely understood. There is no question that some animals use the sun or stars to find their way, but exactly *how* they do so is still a mystery.

Many instances of animal direction-finding cannot be explained at all on the basis of present knowledge. Ordinarily, migrating birds lose their way when the skies are

International Pacific Salmon Fisheries Commission

Swimming together in schools, migrating salmon return to the cold, swift-running stream in Canada where they were born.

International Pacific Salmon Fisheries Commission

Males and females pair off as the salmon prepare to spawn. Despite many theories, no one knows exactly how salmon find their way back to their home stream.

overcast. Yet some birds have been known to maintain a true course through dense fogs, even though they could not see the sky or the ground. In at least one laboratory experiment, warblers chose the correct migratory direction in a closed room, where the sky was not visible. There is some evidence that the birds may have been guided by the earth's magnetic field, but this is not clearly established.

Studies of migrating salmon show how difficult the question of animal direction-finding can be. Experiments suggest that on clear days, salmon can use the sun as a navigational guide. Yet there aren't many clear days along their migration routes; usually, the sun is hidden by fog, mist, haze, or clouds. Other experiments have demonstrated that salmon possess an acute sense of smell. Since every body of water has its own chemical composition, it is possible that the fish remember their home stream from babyhood, somehow detect its smell as they approach the coast, and follow this smell back to their birthplace. According to still another theory, salmon are sensitive to electricity and may be guided by electromagnetic cues from ocean curents. The fact is, no one really knows how these fish find their way back to the fresh-water streams where they were born.

While scientists have learned a great deal about animal migrations, many mysteries remain. Future discoveries in this field may prove even more dramatic than those of the recent past.

4.

The Invisible Boundaries of Home

The first robin of spring drops suddenly from the sky one sunny April morning. He alights on a bush and sings softly. Then he flies to the top of a nearby tree and sings again, but this time, his song is louder.

Before long, he picks out several favorite "singing posts." As he returns again and again to the same bushtop and tree branch, the same fencepost and telephone pole, his call rings out across the countryside.

To human ears, it sounds as though the robin is joyously greeting spring. Yet scientists have found that his song delivers quite a different message.

Staking a Claim

Among most species, it is the male bird who sings. His song is a sharp warning to other males. At the top of his voice, he is claiming property rights to an exclusive territory where he and his future mate will build their nest and raise their young.

If another male trespasses on his land, the owner sings more loudly than ever. And if the rival bird doesn't retreat, the property owner flies to the attack—singing on the wing.

Male birds begin to compete for territories as soon as

Philip Strobridge from National Audubon Society

Robins fighting over territorial rights.

they return from their winter migration. A newcomer usually claims as much land as he can defend against his rivals. He patrols that area as diligently as a watchdog, flying back and forth on the lookout for trespassers.

Two rivals may chase each other from one territory to another and back again. Sometimes, fights break out. The birds attack with beaks and legs, battling in mid-air, and may even fall to the ground while grappling. These fights rarely result in injury, however. For the most part, the birds simply threaten each other, attacking and fleeing in turn. Usually, it is the trespasser who finally retreats to his home ground.

The final size of a territory depends partly on a bird's success in driving off his rivals. He may attempt to claim several acres at first, but as he encounters nearby males, the size of his territory is narrowed. Gradually, the "no-man's land" between territories disappears. Definite boundaries are established. These boundaries are invisible, yet each bird knows exactly where his own territory ends and another begins.

The size of a territory also depends on the particular kind of bird and the availability of food. A golden eagle, which ranges far afield in its search for food, may dominate a territory covering 35 square miles or more. A typical American robin, on the other hand, can get along quite well with an acre or less. Some birds, such as the English sparrow, defend only the area in the immediate vicinity of their nests.

Scientists define a territory as any area which an animal defends against other members of its species. This kind of behavior occurs widely throughout the animal kingdom. We do not know how widely, because new examples are constantly being discovered. It seems, however, that territories are established by most birds, and by many mammals and fish. Scientists have even observed territorial behavior among frogs, lizards, insects, and crabs.

On the Galápagos Islands in the Pacific, marine iguanas clash head-on as they fight over territories. These big lizards swarm by the thousands over the island's rocky beaches. During the mating season, each male stakes out a territory covering a few square yards of rock. When another male approaches, the owner of the territory opens his mouth, nods his head, and starts to parade back and forth. This is a warning. If the trespasser doesn't get out, the land owner lowers his head and rushes forward. The intruder lowers his head too, and the two lizards collide.

On the Galapagos Islands, a marine iguana defends his territory against a rival male. As the rival approaches (a), the owner of the territory opens his mouth, nods his head, and struts back and forth. Then he lunges forward (b), clashing head-on with the intruder. The two iguanas attempt to push each other backward until the intruder finally surrenders by dropping to his belly (c).

Now they try to push each other backwards. If neither one gives way, they both back up, nod at each other, and attack again. The struggle goes on until one of the iguanas "surrenders" by dropping to his belly. The winner immediately stops charging and permits the loser to get up and slink away.

The stickleback, a common fish about the size of your little finger, defends an underwater territory. During the winter, these fish stay together in large schools. In early spring, they migrate from areas in deep fresh water or along the coast to shallow, fresh-water spawning grounds. Then the schools disband as each male goes off by himself to claim his territory.

At the bottom of a pool or stream, a three-spined stickleback builds a tube-shaped nest, using only his mouth as a tool. Standing practically on his head, he sucks up sand, swims away, spits out the sand, then returns to get some more. After digging a pit, he gathers bits and pieces of water plants, drops them into the pit, glues them together with a sticky fluid released by his kidneys, and shapes the nest by rubbing his body against it. After a week or so, he has created a neat submarine tunnel just big enough for a female to enter and deposit her eggs.

While working on his nest, a stickleback will not tolerate interference. He will attack any rival male who invades his territory and will even chase away trespassing females.

During this period, the male gradually changes color. In winter, he is a drab grayish-green. By the time he finishes his nest, his back has turned bluish-white and his belly bright red. This color change is brought about by the rising level of sex hormones in his blood—the same hormones that stimulate him to leave his school, stake out his territory, and build his nest.

Scientists have discovered a close link between male sex hormones and aggressive territorial behavior. Injections of the appropriate hormones will stimulate the fighting instincts of baby chicks, rats, rabbits, and other immature animals long before they are old enough to claim and defend territories of their own.

from Social Behavior in Animals *by N. Tinbergen. Methuen & Co. Ltd.*

Sticklebacks fighting: a male will attack any rival which approaches his nest.

Many animals claim territories only during the mating season. Others live in the same territory all year long. Often, a permanent territory is occupied by a large family group and is defended by adult males in the group. A wolf pack, roaming through its home ground in search of food, will attack any strange wolf on sight. A beaver colony is strictly off-limits to beavers from "foreign" colonies. A pack of rats will sometimes kill trespassing rats from other packs.

Territorial behavior serves a useful function: it "spaces out" animals in the area they occupy. This prevents overcrowding and helps regulate the food supply. Inside the invisible boundaries of home, animals do not have to compete for food with others of their kind. They can mate and raise their young without interference.

Territories also provide protection. By being scattered over a large area instead of crowded together in one place, animals have a better chance to conceal themselves and avoid their enemies.

Although territories are usually claimed and defended by males, there are some species in which the female is the most aggressive. In Venezuela, tiny female frogs stake out mating territories along the banks of streams and attack other females who venture too close. When a rival approaches, one of these frogs will raise her head, expose her bright yellow throat, and pulsate it rapidly. If the rival doesn't retreat, the owner of the territory jumps her and the two lady frogs wrestle until one or the other gives up and hops away.

PROJECT
Mapping Underwater Territories

Many common aquarium fish stake out underwater territories. Paradise fish, Siamese fighting fish, and various species of cichlids (such as ports, jewel fish, and Jack Dempseys) are obtainable in most pet shops and can be used for studies of territorial behavior. Males of these species generally reach breeding age before they are a year old. At this time, a male will claim his territory and defend it against all rival males.

1. For this project you will need a twenty gallon tank. Divide the tank into two sections with a glass partition. Ask your pet shop for two males that are beginning to exhibit

territorial behavior and place one fish on either side of the partition. (If you have never raised tropical fish, you should first read a book on aquarium management. Ask your pet shop to recommend one, or see the following: *Tropical Fish Book,* H. R. Axelrod, Fawcett World Library; *Breeding Aquarium Fish,* W. Wickler, D. Van Nostrand Co. Both available in paperback.)

2. In a few days, after each fish has become accustomed to its half of the tank, remove the partition. Does each male remain in its half of the tank? How do the fish respond when they meet in the middle of the tank?

3. Lay a piece of clean glass or Plexiglas over the top of the tank. Use a felt tip marker to draw a dotted line on the glass, indicating where the partition had been. As you watch the fish through the top of the tank, make a mark on the transparent cover above each point where the fish meet in an aggressive encounter. After marking a dozen or more encounters, you should be able to draw a new line representing the boundary between the territories each fish has claimed.

4. Repeat this procedure each day for several days. Does the boundary remain the same? Does either fish extend the boundaries of its territory beyond the half of the tank it had

originally occupied? What do you think would happen if the fish had not started out with equal space in the tank?

5. Lower a mirror into each male's territory. Do the fish respond aggressively to their own image?

6. Catch the fish and place them in separate glass jars. Now place both jars inside the territory of one male. How does each fish respond? Move the jars to the territory on the opposite side of the tank. What differences do you see in the fish's responses? Does each fish seem more confident and aggressive while inside its own territory?

7. This project can also be conducted with three or four males of the same species. In this case, map the territory claimed by each of the males. However, to allow the fish sufficient space for their territories, no more than four small males should be placed in a twenty gallon tank.

Signals of Aggression

When a Venezuelan frog pulsates her bright yellow throat, she is warning her rival to stay away. A marine iguana warns his rival by nodding his head and parading back and forth. A robin sings at the top of his voice: "Keep out! Keep out!"

At Oxford University, Dr. David Lack found that an English robin also recognizes another warning signal. One spring morning, Dr. Lack went quietly into his garden carrying a stuffed robin which he had purchased for fifteen cents. He placed the stuffed bird on a bush, then retreated inside the house and watched through a window.

Not long before, a real robin had claimed the scientist's garden as his exclusive territory. As soon as the robin spotted the fifteen-cent dummy, he sang loudly to drive the intruder away. But the dummy refused to move. Suddenly the robin swooped down from a tree, passed over the bush like a dive bomber, and attacked. He tore off the dummy's head, leaving little more than a clump of red breast feathers hanging from the bush.

Much to Dr. Lack's surprise, the robin continued with his fierce assault, pecking away at the tattered breast feathers and singing violently. Was this aggressive bird responding to the color of the dummy's feathers?

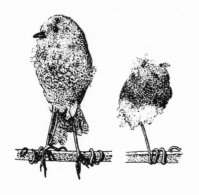

from Social Behavior in Animals
by N. Tinbergen. Methuen & Co. Ltd.

An English robin will ignore a
stuffed bird which lacks a red
breast (*left*), but will attack a
clump of red breast feathers
(*right*).

Dr. Lack bought another stuffed robin and painted its
red breast brown before planting it on the same bush.
This time, the robin paid no attention to the stuffed bird.

Then Dr. Lack tied a clump of red breast feathers to a
wire and attached the feathers to the bush. These feathers
didn't look anything like a real bird, yet the scientist was
scarcely out of the way before the robin swooped down
from his tree and attacked again. The mere sight of red
breast feathers had triggered the bird's aggressive instincts.

To an English robin, the sight of red breast feathers is
as much a warning signal as the sound of a male's territorial song. When a male is defending his territory, he will
fly instantly toward the source of a rival's song, but will
not attack until he actually sees the rival's red breast. And
before attacking, he will display his own red breast as a
final warning to the trespassing bird.

Bright colors and markings play an important role in
the territorial behavior of many birds. A red-winged
blackbird puffs up his red shoulder patches when he con-
fronts a rival. A European chaffinch displays white shoulder patches as his fighting banners. An American wood-
pecker, the yellow-shafted flicker, shows a rival his black
"mustache."

Female flickers do not have this distinguishing mark. Dr. G. K. Noble captured a female one summer and painted a black mustache across her face. When the bird was returned to her nesting territory, her mate didn't recognize her. He attacked—just as he would attack any rival male—and drove her away. After Dr. Noble removed the mustache from the female's face, her mate welcomed her back home.

If a miror is placed inside a bird's territory, the bird will often mistake its image for a rival male and will attack the mirror. Quite frequently, a bird that has claimed a territory near a house will flutter against the window panes, trying to drive away its own reflection.

Fish also respond to the bright colors, markings, and patterns of their rivals. We have already seen how a three-spined stickleback undergoes a dramatic color change

No trespassing! A grouper warns away a rival by raising his fins, opening his mouth, and producing a drumming sound with his air bladder.

William M. Stephens

during the nesting season: his belly turns bright red. Like
a robin's red breast, the stickleback's red belly is his battle
flag.

Experimenting with these fish at Oxford University,
Dr. Niko Tinbergen found that a male will attack a
wooden model which has been painted red underneath—
even if the model isn't shaped like a real fish. However,
the same male will ignore a wooden model which looks
exactly like a stickleback, but is *not* painted red underneath.

The color red is such a powerful stimulus to a male
stickleback, he will sometimes try to attack any red object
he sees. Dr. Tinbergen kept his experimental fish in a row
of glass tanks set in front of the laboratory windows. On
the street outside, mail trucks passed by several times a
day. The trucks were painted red, and Dr. Tinbergen
tells how the fish responded:

"All the males which I observed even 'attacked' the red
mail vans passing about a hundred yards away; that is to

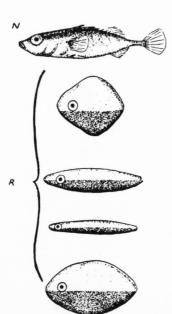

from Social Behavior in Animals
by N. Tinbergen. Methuen & Co. Ltd.

A three-spined stickleback will
ignore a perfectly shaped wooden
model which lacks a red "belly"
(N), but will attack crude wood-
en models which are painted red
underneath (R).

say, they raised their dorsal spines and made frantic efforts to reach the vans, which of course was prevented by the glass wall of the aquarium. When a van passed the laboratory where a row of twenty aquaria were situated along the large windows, all males dashed toward the window side of their tanks and followed the van from one corner of their tank to the other."

Color signals also trigger the territorial instincts of many reptiles and insects. A male fence lizard has brilliant blue stripes down both sides of his body. If similar stripes are painted on a female, she will be attacked by any male whose mating territory she enters. On the other hand, if a male's stripes are covered up, and if this disguised male is placed inside a rival's territory, the owner of the territory will mistake the intruder for a female and will attempt to woo him.

Most mammals are color blind, yet they possess an acute sense of smell. Living in a world filled with vivid and meaningful odors, they rely largely on scent-signals to mark their territories and to recognize the territories of others.

Mammals often have special scent-producing glands. In the American deer, these glands are located near the hoof. When a deer rubs its hoof on the ground or against a tree, the glands release a strong-smelling substance which serves as the deer's personal mark of ownership. Another deer, sniffing this odor, will usually steer clear of the owner's territory.

Male rabbits have scent-producing glands beneath the chin and under the tail. A male constantly rubs his chin

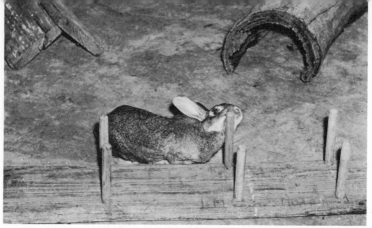

E. Slater, Division of Wildlife Research, CSIRO, Australia

A rabbit marks objects in his territory with scent produced by special glands under his chin.

over the entrance to his burrow, and against branches, bushes, blades of grass, and other objects in his territory. Males also use their scent glands to mark their mates and their young. As a result, all members of the same family group carry the same distinctive smell and will attack strange rabbits who smell different.

Certain insects also use their sense of smell to detect the presence of outsiders. A bee hive is a territory defended by a large colony of bees. Guard bees maintain a vigil at the entrance to the hive and use their long antennae to examine all incoming bees. Strangers are recognized by their foreign odors and are promptly driven away.

Rules of Combat

It might seem that fighting among territorial animals would constantly lead to serious injury and even death, but this isn't the case. Once an animal has successfully claimed a territory, a simple warning is usually enough to discourage any rivals.

In the heart of his home territory, an animal often seems fearless and invincible. As he approaches the boundaries of his territory, however, he becomes more cautious. If he meets a rival along the boundary, he seems torn between the urge to attack and the urge to escape. And once he ventures into foreign territory, he is at a great disadvantage and is easily driven away.

In a study of wild Australian rabbits, scientists found that these animals move about confidently inside their own territory. In a strange territory, however, a rabbit's behavior changes. He does not attempt to mark objects with his own scent, and he doesn't even try to feed. Instead, he is constantly on the alert—his neck stretched and his nostrils quivering as he sniffs the unfamiliar odors. If he is suddenly challenged by one of the rabbits living in that territory, he will run away without a fight—even if the challenger is only half-grown.

When two birds meet in a dispute over territory, they may fly at each other and make a lot of noise. But this aerial display is mostly bluff. After the rivals warn and threaten each other, the trespasser usually turns tail and escapes, while the owner of the territory remains in possession of his property.

Male prairie chickens in a territorial dispute. *Charles W. Schwartz*

In his experiments with English robins, Dr. David Lack placed a male in a cage and left the cage in the middle of the bird's own territory. Before long, another male flew into the territory and cautiously approached the cage. Even though the captive robin was behind bars, he defended his territory by singing loudly. Surprisingly enough, this was all that was needed to drive the intruder away.

Afterwards, Dr. Lack moved the caged bird to another robin's territory. When the owner of the territory showed up to investigate, the captive robin cowered in his cage— terrified because he could not escape. On foreign ground, all his self-confidence had disappeared.

Even when rivals actually fight, they do not usually inflict serious injury. In fact, they seem to obey certain instinctive rules of combat which permit them to go through all the motions of fighting without really harming each other.

Rattlesnakes could kill each other with a single bite. But when they meet in combat, they never bite. As two snakes approach each other, they lift their long bodies into the air, press their heads and necks together, and start pushing. An "Indian wrestling" match results as each snake tries to force his rival sideways and down to the ground. The winner pins the loser to the ground with the weight of his body. Then he lets the loser escape— without trying to bite him.

Antelope fight territorial duels with their long horns. At first, two rivals will fence with the upper parts of their horns, as though they are testing each other's courage and strength. Then they clash forehead to forehead, lock their

Indian antelope duel with their horns but rarely injure each other.

horns together, and push back and forth until one of the animals gives up. Although their horns are as sharp as swords, they rarely gore each other.

The instinctive nature of these pushing contests was illustrated by a male antelope at a German zoo. This bull had lost his horns. Even so, he followed all the rules of combat typical of his kind. When dueling with another male, he struck at his opponent's horns from the exact distance at which his non-existent horns would have made contact. His opponents, in turn, acted as though his horns were still in place; they stayed a certain distance away and responded to his imaginary blows.

Fights between rival animals usually end when one of the combatants indicates that he is ready to "surrender." When two wolves fight, they start to bite each other. As soon as one wolf begins to lose, he exposes his throat—the most vulnerable part of his body. This act of submission immediately stops the other wolf from attacking. The winner backs up and stands by—ready to attack again—until the loser gets up and runs away.

Is Man Territorial?

The discovery of territorial behavior among animals has revived an old controversy about human beings. Some scientists suggest that we humans may have inherited aggressive territorial instincts from our remote ancestors.

According to this theory, early man competed for territories just as animals do. Brandishing crude stone weapons, driven by impulses he could neither understand nor control, the cave dweller of the prehistoric past defended his territorial boundaries against all outsiders. This aggressive instinct, the theory suggests, still exists in human beings. It is an underlying cause of conflict among individuals and warfare among nations.

Are aggression and warfare built into human nature? Is it more natural for us to live peacefully with our neighbors, or to bash them over the head?

No one can answer these questions with absolute certainty. However, many scientists have rejected the notion that men and animals share similar territorial instincts. This idea, they argue, is not supported by the evidence at hand. Although some animals defend territories, others do not. Chimpanzees and gorillas, usually considered man's closest non-human relatives, display no clear-cut evidence of a territorial instinct.

Even if they did, it would not necessarily mean that man possesses the same instinct. Man is unique among living creatures because his behavior is determined primarily by what he learns. His unmatched ability to learn has liberated him from the trigger-like reactions of instinct and has given him the power to make conscious decisions.

Among humans, complex patterns of behavior are passed along from one generation to the next by means of spoken and written language. A child learns to adapt to the customs and traditions of his group. History and culture play such a powerful role in shaping the human personality, man seems to retain few, if any, instinctive patterns of behavior.

According to this point of view, men fight each other not because of instinct, as animals do, but because of their cultural training. If this is so, then it is society that must be changed—and not human nature—if we want to eliminate aggression and warfare from human history.

5.

Animal Courtship

When a male bird hears another male sing, he recognizes that song as a warning and usually steers clear of his rival's territory. An unattached female reacts differently. To her, the same song is an invitation. She seems to know that a singing male is a successful property owner, able to support a family, and she flies over to investigate.

Instead of welcoming her, the male may try to chase her away. Determined to defend his newly acquired territory, he threatens all trespassers—inquisitive females as well as rival males. And no wonder. In nearly half of all species of birds, males and females look so much alike that not even another bird can tell the difference.

Then how does a look-alike female identify herself?

The Courtship of Birds

At first glance, there is no difference between male and female English robins. Both have red breasts—and red breast feathers are what trigger the male's fighting instincts.

When a female flies into a male's territory, he reacts aggressively at first. He sings loudly, puffs out his red breast feathers, jerks his head up and down, and makes other threatening motions. Challenged in this way, a tres-

Spring song; to a rival male, a warning; to an unattached female, an invitation.

passing male would either retreat from the territory or would return the owner's threats. A female does neither. She won't leave, and she gives no sign that she is willing to fight.

The male seems puzzled. He darts about from tree to tree, sings at the top of his voice, and threatens the female again. What does she do? She flies meekly after him, still refusing to fight or flee.

In this way, the female gradually disarms the male. His attitude begins to change from aggression to acceptance. He may suddenly preen his feathers and strut about. And instead of threatening the female or flying away from her, he begins to follow her. She has identified herself not by her appearance, but by her *behavior*.

Once the male accepts the female, the two robins will peacefully share the same territory for two or three months without paying much attention to each other. Toward the end of their "engagement" period, the female begins to build a nest of moss and leaves. Now the male shows his first real interest in courtship. As the nest takes shape, he brings the female a gift.

He finds a small insect and carries it over to her. She responds like a baby robin—crouching down, fluttering her wings, and stretching her neck as if she is begging for food.

The female's begging behavior has nothing to do with hunger. Scientists have found that a female will beg from her mate even if she is standing on a food-laden table. One female took an insect from a scientist's hand, carried it over to her mate, and dropped it at his feet. Then she opened her mouth and fluttered her wings until he picked up the food and gave it to her.

Courtship feeding is quite common among birds. A male tern offers a small fish to a female and the birds soar into the air, passing the fish back and forth as they fly over their colony. Even a domestic rooster will "find" food for a hen and cluck over it invitingly until the hen comes running.

Among most birds, the female must first gain the acceptance of her future mate. He may threaten and chase her until she finally conquers his aggressive instincts. Once a pair is formed, however, it is the male who usually plays the most active role in courtship.

Many males engage in elaborate courtship displays. Accomplished fliers, such as the skylark, perform intricate aerial maneuvers to impress their mates. Sparrows and other drab-coated males often rely on their singing talents. Brightly colored males frequently strut and pose during courtship, showing off their plumage. A peacock will spread his gorgeous tail feathers, clatter his quills together, scream loudly, and turn slowly around in front of a female. These displays help intensify the mating drive by increasing the flow of sex hormones inside each bird's body.

PROJECT
Investigate the Courtship Behavior of Pigeons

The courtship behavior of the domestic pigeon can be observed in the streets and parks of most cities. Find an open area where pigeons can gather to feed without being disturbed by traffic or pedestrians. You will probably find it easy to attract pigeons to the area by scattering bread crumbs. During the spring and summer, many of these birds will be in a mating mood. The males may already have claimed nesting sites nearby on sheltered ledges or behind the ornamental stonework of older buildings. When these males arrive at the feeding area, they will often show more interest in attracting a mate than in feeding.

1. Male and female pigeons are somewhat similar in appearance. However, you should be able to identify them by their behavior. A male will land near a female who is feeding quietly and will run up to her with his head lowered and his neck feathers ruffled. Note how he bows to her and follows her about with his head bobbing and his tail feathers sweeping the ground. Watch him draw himself up to his full height and bow again and again. As he does this, he utters a deep *coo-roo-cuh-t'coo*.

2. Observe the coloring of the male's feathers. Does his display seem to show off certain aspects of his coloring?

3. Note the sequence of the male's courtship responses as they occur one after another. Do they always occur in the same order?

4. Do the male's cooing sounds always occur during the same part of his display? What movement precedes the coos? What follows them?

5. Does the male display before more than one female?

6. Observe the female's behavior. How does she respond to the male's display?

If the female is not ready to mate, she will ignore her suitor or move away from him. Even if she is in a mating mood, it may be some time before she shows any interest. Eventually, however, you may see a female respond to the attention she is getting by ruffling her neck feathers, spreading her tail, and opening her wings slightly at the shoulders. Her response is a cue to the male. He will stop his strutting and bowing and will suddenly thrust his beak beneath his wing, as if he intended to preen his feathers. This act signals the female, who so far has shyly kept her distance. While the male's head is turned, she approaches him and presses her body against his. When the male turns his head toward her again, she will thrust her beak into his mouth like a baby pigeon begging for food. With beaks interlocked, the pair will bob their heads up and down. After this billing display is over, the birds will mate and fly away to build a nest and raise their young.

Birds of paradise, found in New Guinea, are famous for their flamboyant courtship displays. A male blue bird of paradise has sky-blue wings, a long black tail, and a splendid underside of blue, black, and azure with high-lights of chestnut and purple. During courtship, he stands perched on a branch, his feathers slightly raised and his wings quivering. He bows first to one side, then to the other. Back and forth he moves, bowing more deeply each time, until his beak finally touches the branch he is stand-ing on. Then he swings around and hangs upside down, his wings spread wide, his breast feathers fluffed out, and his head turned toward one shoulder. As he hangs there, his entire body begins to quiver. Suddenly, his breast feathers move apart, revealing a long black band with a fiery red border which runs across the middle of his body.

Many birds dance during courtship. The Australian lyre bird not only dances, but includes songs and imita-tions as part of his performance. In his woodland terri-tory, he makes several small clearings, scraping leaves and earth together to form platforms. Each platform becomes a stage. When the lyre bird mounts one of his stages, he spreads his fan-like tail, throws it over his head like a veil, and turns in a half-circle. Then he stands high on his toes

An Australian lyre bird clears the woodland stage where he will perform his courtship ceremony.

Spreading his fan-like tail, he throws it over his head and turns in a half-circle.

Australian News and Information Bureau

Standing on tiptoe, the lyre bird snaps his tail closed and then spreads it open again.

and shakes his feathers. He turns again and again, jumping forward and stepping back, snapping his tail closed, then spreading it open again. During this dance, he sings the melodic courtship song of his species and also imitates the calls of other birds and animals. Sometimes a male will go from one clearing to another, singing and dancing on each of his stages as his mate, not far away, watches intently through the trees.

Some birds gather in large groups to parade and perform during the mating season. North American prairie chickens visit special dancing arenas every spring. The females stand aside and watch as thirty or forty males compete for attention. The males strut about, jump high into the air, inflate their orange neck sacks, and make deep booming sounds.

Similar courtship gatherings are held by sharp-tailed grouse. Here again, the males perform for the females. Holding their heads down, spreading their wings, and rattling their tail feathers, they shuffle back and forth, stamping their feet and uttering deep pigeon-like coos. All the males perform the same steps at the same time. When one bird stamps, they all stamp; when one stops, they all stop and stand motionless. The plains Indians copied some of their ritual dances from these birds and others like them.

Though male birds usually play the leading role in courtship, there are some exceptions. In East Africa, female ostriches gather in small groups, fluff out their feathers, and perform high-stepping dances for the benefit of nearby males. Every so often a female will stop dancing, leave her group, and start racing across the grassy plain as a male pursues her.

A courtship display is a form of animal language. It involves a series of signals which enable males and females to recognize each other as members of the same species.

In North America alone, there are some 40 different species of ducks. Some are similar in appearance and inhabit the same general areas, yet no two species have identical courtship displays. If a female mallard duck happened to meet a male ruddy duck, she would not understand his courtship signals and would not recognize him as a potential mate.

Scientists have found that courtship displays are largely instinctive. A male duck can be hatched in an incubator and raised in isolation, yet the first time he is in the right situation, he will perform all the displays typical of his species without making a single mistake. Even if a duckling grows up with foster parents and broodmates of a different species, he will not imitate their displays, but will perform those of his own parents, whom he has never seen. Similar experiments with various kinds of insects, fish and mammals suggest that courtship displays are as much a part of an animal's inheritance as the color of its eyes and shape of its body.

Underwater Courtship

Many fish swim through the ocean in large schools. During the spawning season, males and females are stimulated by changes in temperature or other factors to release their sperm and eggs into the water. Fertilization occurs

Drumming his breast with his bill, a male ruddy duck creates a "bubbling" display which attracts females and warns away rival males.

as clouds of sex cells mingle in the sea. For these fish, elaborate courtship ceremonies are not necessary.

Some fish do pair off to spawn, however. In most cases, they inhabit shallow coastal waters or fresh-water lakes and streams, where their eggs and sperm might easily drift away or be washed ashore. Sometimes their courtship behavior is strikingly similar to that of birds.

A male American sunfish claims a territory near the bank of a lake or pond and uses his tail to scoop out a shallow nesting hole in the mud. When an eligible female swims into the territory, the male tries to chase her away —just as he chases away rival males. But the female refuses to leave. Instead, she swims in a circle around the nesting hollow, and before long, the male begins to follow her. He follows her around and around until both fish release their eggs and sperm into the nest.

A male Siamese fighting fish builds a frothy nest of floating bubbles. He produces these tough, sticky bubbles in his mouth and blows them into the water beneath a leaf or some other object floating on the surface. Then he waits quietly with his fins folded until another fighting fish approaches.

Swimming in smaller and smaller circles beneath their nest of floating bubbles, male and female fighting fish release their eggs and sperm into the water. The fertilized eggs can be seen sinking toward the bottom of the aquarium tank.

The male pursues the eggs, scoops them into his mouth . . .

. . . and blows them into the midst of his bubble nest.

Ordinarily, the male is a rather dull brownish gray. But when he sights a rival, his fins bristle, his gill covers pop out, and his body glows with brilliant metallic hues. Rival males often engage in bloody battles. Ramming each other with gaping mouths, they lock jaws and struggle violently in the water. Sometimes they rip each other's fins off and bite patches from each other's flanks. The battle continues until one of the combatants finally gives up and escapes.

A male also assumes his fighting colors when he sights a female. However, she immediately folds her fins—indicating that she will not fight back. Slowly, she swims toward the male and undergoes a modest color change of her own.

The male seems torn between his urge to attack an intruder and the conflicting urge to attract a mate. He may chase the female at first, but eventually he gives in to his mating urge and leads her under his floating nest. The two fish swim rapidly beneath the bubbles in smaller and smaller circles; their colors become increasingly brighter; and finally, their bodies seem to intertwine. As the female sheds her eggs, they begin to sink toward the bottom like tiny glass beads. The male swims after them, scoops the eggs into his mouth, returns to his nest, and blows the eggs into the midst of the floating bubbles.

No fish has been studied more carefully than the little three-spined stickleback. We have already seen how a male stickleback builds a tube-shaped nest from bits and pieces of water plants. He recognizes rival males by their bright red bellies, and attacks them on sight. A female lacks this red belly. When she is ready to spawn, she de-

from Social Behavior in Animals
by N. Tinbergen. Methuen & Co. Ltd.

The zig-zag courtship dance of a
three-spined stickleback.

velops a brilliant silvery gloss and her body swells with
eggs.

As a female approaches a male's territory, she empha-
sizes her swollen shape by raising her head and tail. The
male responds by performing a zig-zag courtship dance.
He dances toward the female and all around her, and
finally leads her to his nest. With his snout, he points to
the entrance. She pushes past him and enters the narrow
opening alone, her head protruding from one end of the
nest, her tail from the other.

Now the male uses his snout to nudge the female's body
near the base of her tail, causing her to spawn. Then he
chases her away and enters the nest himself to fertilize the
eggs.

When Dr. Niko Tinbergen studied these fish at Oxford University, he found that a male will court a crude wooden model which appears to have an egg-swollen body. As soon as the male sees such a model, he swims over to it and performs his zig-zag dance. If the model is pushed toward him, he turns around and leads it to his nest. And if the model is pushed into the nest, he nudges the base of its "tail" with his snout.

In the same way, a female will follow a crude wooden model which is painted red underneath and is pushed through the water in a zig-zag fashion. If the model "points" to the entrance of a nest, the female swims inside. And if the experimenter nudges the base of her tail with a glass rod, she lays her eggs.

For the stickleback, as for most animals, courtship is a chain reaction in which one mating signal leads automatically to the next.

Courtship among Insects and Spiders

In the tall grass on a warm summer evening, you can sometimes see hundreds of lights flashing on and off. Each tiny pinpoint of light shines for a split second and then goes out, only to be replaced by another light not far away. All around you, wherever you look, lights flash on and off endlessly through the night.

These are fireflies exchanging mating signals. Their bright glow is produced by special organs in their abdomens. Each species of firefly has a distinct signal code which enables males and females to find each other in the dark. Males of one species flash at intervals of 5.8 seconds, for example. Nearby females flash in reply at the same intervals, but exactly two seconds later. No other species uses precisely the same code.

Female moths use scent-producing glands to send out mating signals. The scent-signals are picked up by two large feather-like antennae protruding from the male's head. These antennae are so sensitive, a male can detect the attracting scent of a female from as far as three miles away. Like an airplane on automatic control, he will follow the scent into a town, ignore hundreds of competing odors, and fly directly to the female. Moth collectors often place a captive female inside a ventilated box. Before long, male moths fly into the vicinity and begin to flutter around the box.

Sound signals are used widely in the courtship of insects. A male mosquito is attracted to a female by the whirring hum of her wings. In a laboratory experiment, males will zero in on a vibrating tuning fork which produces the same humming sound.

Most insects produce mating sounds by rubbing one part of their body against another. Locusts rub their legs against their wings, just as a violinist runs his bow across the strings. Crickets and katydids scrape their wings together, creating the chirping symphonies heard on many a summer's night.

Crickets have been called the master musicians of the insect world. There are about 2500 known species of crickets, and as many as 30 or 40 different species may be sending out musical signals in the same general area at the same time. Yet there is no confusion, since each species has its own distinct calls. A female responds only to the calls made by males of her own species. Like most in-

A male praying mantis bows before the female he is courting. After mating, the female often devours her partner.

sects, crickets do not hatch from the egg until long after all individuals of the previous generation have died. As a result, they have no chance to imitate the calls of older, experienced crickets. Yet the first time a male cricket tries to chirp, he gives exactly the right chirp for his species. And the first time a female hears this call, she knows what it means.

A number of insects present gifts to their mates. Certain flies mate only after the male brings the female some food. He catches an insect smaller than himself and wraps it with silk threads secreted from glands on his front legs. Then he flies over to a female and hands her his gift package.

Courtship feeding is fairly common among spiders. Female spiders are usually larger and more ferocious than males of the same species. They are apt to pounce on and devour any small living creature that comes their way— including their prospective mates. For this reason, self-defense plays a crucial role in the mating behavior of these males. In one species, the male catches a fly, wraps it neatly in a web, and approaches the female cautiously, holding the gift out in front of him. While the female is busy unwrapping the fly, the male can mate with her safely.

Many male spiders will not approach a female until they have identified themselves from a distance. Sometimes the male uses his legs to drum a particular pattern of vibrations on the female's web; she recognizes these vibrations as a mating signal rather than the struggles of a captured prey, and she withholds her hungry attack. Among spiders which do not build webs but hunt actively for their food, the male may signal by making elaborate motions with his legs, in a kind of semaphore code, or by dancing. Some male spiders lift their legs high in the air and skip from side to side, while others win a female's favor by twirling about on tiptoe.

The Courtship of Mammals

Courtship signals usually take advantage of an animal's best-developed senses. Birds have excellent color vision and often display their brilliant plumage. Since most mammals are color blind, they rely largely on scent-signals during courtship, just as they rely on scent-signals to mark their territories. When the mating season begins, special scent-producing glands become active in both males and females of many species. The distinctive odors produced by these glands help members of the same species identify each other and also stimulate their urge to mate.

Mammalian courtship often begins with a chase. The chase may be brief and uncomplicated, or it may involve elaborate movements and ceremonies. A male hedgehog begins to circle his mate after chasing and catching her. He keeps this up for hours, huffing and puffing and extending his snout as he walks tirelessly around the female.

The courtship chase of some squirrels is a stop and start affair. The male chases the female until she suddenly stops short. He stops too. Both squirrels beat their paws on the ground and clash their teeth together. Then they start running again.

Cottontail rabbits engage in hopping contests during courtship. A male and female will face each other. Then one leaps into the air while the other dashes underneath. Turning around and facing each other again, they repeat this "leap-frog" ceremony many times.

Some male mammals, such as deer, elk and sea lions, attempt to herd females into harems during the mating season. This behavior has been studied closely among red deer. A single stag will collect as large a harem as he possibly can by running around the females in a circle. He circles them continuously, stopping occasionally to paw the ground, then running again and roaring loudly every few seconds. The roar is a challenge to rival stags who constantly rush in and try to steal females from the harem. A large harem may suddenly become a small one or may even disappear, for as a stag is fighting with one rival,

A bull elk guards his harem.

other males will slip quietly into his harem to divide the females among themselves and drive them away.

Fights between rival males are quite common among mammals, and in some species, fights also occur between males and females. Rats and mice often engage in rough-and-tumble battles, wrestling, biting and scratching each other before they are ready to mate.

Sometimes, a male and female who seem to be fighting may actually be playing. A pair of badgers will wrestle vigorously during courtship, turning somersaults in a swirling mass of fur, then dashing off at great speed as they chase each other through clearings and around trees. Two sea otters will swim out to the fringes of their herd, where they dive, leap into the air, spin around, and chase each other back and forth through the waves.

Naturalists are often impressed by what appear to be genuine displays of affection during the courtship of some mammals. Black bears stand upright and hug each other fondly. Giraffes nuzzle each other tenderly, rubbing their heads and necks together. Elephants "kiss" with their trunks and often spend weeks in close companionship before they are ready to mate. Dolphins also have long periods of courtship. They swim everywhere together, feed side by side, and frequently nuzzle each other with their snouts or gently bite their partner's flippers. If the female wanders too far away, the male calls her back with short, sharp yelps.

A few mammals, including foxes, wolves, beavers, and certain apes, seem to form mating pairs which may last for many years. Some foxes are believed to mate for life. It is said that if one of the pair dies, the other will refuse to accept another mate.

Like other animals, most mammals mate only at certain definite periods, when their glands are producing hormones which cause egg cells to ripen in the female or sperm cells to be formed in the male. Mating cannot be successful unless the animals come together at the right time. They must also belong to the same species. When members of two different species attempt to mate, offspring usually will not result. If they do, these hybrid offspring may be unable to reproduce or even to survive.

Whether courtship is elaborate or simple—whether it involves the spectacular display of the peacock, the zig-zag dance of the stickleback, the musical message of the cricket, or the breathless chase of the badger—it always serves two important functions. Courtship helps intensify the mating drive. And it enables males and females of the same species to identify each other when the time for mating comes around.

6.

Raising a Family

At a single spawning, a female codfish sheds millions of eggs into the waters around her. With this act her responsibilities as a parent end, for she swims away, abandoning her eggs to the perils of the sea. Most of them never hatch. Perhaps one egg in a million survives to become an adult cod.

A female chimpanzee usually has only one infant at each birth. However, she lavishes care upon it—nursing her baby, holding it in her arms, carrying it about, grooming it, protecting it, and seldom letting it out of her sight until it is five or six years old.

As a general rule, mammals and birds make dedicated parents. They have relatively few offspring and provide them with food and protection until the youngsters are

On its own: this hour-old trout gets its first meals from the yolk sac attached to its body. Like most fish, it comes into the world without ever seeing its parents.

Treat Davidson from National Audubon Society

old enough to take care of themselves. Most other animals never even see their offspring. They simply lay large numbers of eggs and then disappear, leaving the eggs to hatch unaided.

Yet there are always exceptions, and we can find devoted animal parents even among insects, reptiles and fish.

Animal Nurseries

Like the cod, most ocean fish shed enormous quantities of eggs into the water and swim away without ever looking back. However, fish that live in sheltered bays and inlets, or in fresh-water lakes and streams, often lay fewer eggs and make special efforts to protect them. Some fish deposit their eggs in natural holes or hollows, in clumps of seaweed, or beneath rocks or gravel. Others dig shallow nesting holes in the mud. And a few enterprising fish, such as the doughty sticklebacks and the Siamese fighting fish, build elaborate nests as nurseries for their eggs and young.

Nests are also built by a few exceptional frogs. A certain South American species folds leaves and cements their edges together, forming little bags which hold enough rainwater for the frogs' developing eggs. Another South American frog collects beeswax and uses it to line holes in trees, making the holes leakproof and providing artificial pools where the eggs can hatch.

Only a small percentage of the earth's staggering variety of insects can be called true nest-builders, yet their nests include some of the architectural wonders of the animal world. Hunting wasps are probably the most accomplished builders among solitary insects. Some hunting wasps dig underground burrows for each egg they lay and camouflage the burrows with pebbles and earth. Others place their nests high above the ground. The mud-dauber fashions hollow tubes of hardened mud and cements these nests to trees, or to the walls or ceiling of a barn. Each mud tube is subdivided into several egg cells. The wasp provisions these cells with paralyzed spiders, providing food for the larvae to eat when they hatch.

Potter wasps also build of mud; however their nests resemble tiny jugs attached to branches or twigs. Each jug has a round body, a narrow neck, a wide lip at the top, and a tight-fitting lid. Before sealing the nest with this lid, the potter wasp deposits a caterpillar in the jug. Then she suspends her egg from the top of the jug by a silken thread, so that the developing egg hangs directly over the paralyzed caterpillar.

The largest and most impressive insect nests, however, are built by the social insects—ants, termites, and some species of bees and wasps. Instead of living alone, as most insects do, social insects spend their lives as members of complex, highly organized societies. Their nests are not simply nurseries for their eggs and young, but are populous insect cities teeming with busy inhabitants.

Honey bees build with wax secreted from glands on their abdomens. The wax combs of a bee hive contain thousands of neat, six-sided cells for the hive's developing eggs and larvae, as well as special storage cells for its supply of honey and pollen. Worker bees buzz tirelessly about the hive, building new combs, tending the eggs and larvae, keeping the hive clean, and ventilating it by fanning their wings. The queen bee works hard too. She may lay as many as 3000 eggs in a single day.

Social wasps build similar nests of a stiff, paper-like material which they manufacture by chewing the fibers of rotten wood and the stems of plants. Yellow-jacket wasps conceal their paper nests in underground hollows, while hornets suspend great paper balls from the branches of trees. Inside the tough outer wrapping of a hornets' nest are layers of paper combs stacked one atop another; each comb contains rows of six-sided egg cells, holding eggs and larvae in various stages of development.

Many ants nest underground. The burrows of leaf-cutting ants may penetrate fifteen feet into the earth, cover an area larger than a football field, and contain sev-

Courtesy of The American Museum of Natural History

A million termites may inhabit this insect skyscraper in northern Kenya. The mound is built of earth and vegetation mixed with the termites' own saliva.

eral million insects crawling back and forth through a vast maze of interlocking tunnels and chambers. But the most impressive insect nests of all, perhaps, are the towering mounds constructed by various termites in Africa and the tropics. Built of earth and vegetation mixed with the termites' own saliva, these insect skyscrapers sometimes rise fifteen or twenty feet into the air. Their thick, sun-baked walls become as hard as concrete —so hard, in fact, the mounds must be blown up with dynamite before the land they stand on can be cleared. Temperature and humidity are controlled by efficient networks of air vents and ducts which bring a constant flow of fresh air into the labyrinth of chambers and corridors inside the mounds, while sloping or overhanging roofs protect the mounds from rain. Some termite mounds look like steeples, turrets, or towers. Others resemble enormous mushrooms or small pyramids. Each species of termite follows its own distinct architectural blueprint—the blueprint of its ancestors—for despite the intricate construction and marvelous engineering of these gigantic insect nests, they are built entirely by instinct.

While nest-building is the exception among insects and fish, it is the general rule among birds. Often, a bird's nest is built by the female alone. Sometimes the male helps out, and occasionally he takes on the entire job himself.

A bird's nest may be as simple as a tern's shallow depression in the sand, as familiar as a robin's mud and grass bowl, as elegant as an oriole's hanging basket, or as sturdy as a cliff swallow's inaccessible mud hut. The smallest nests, built by hummingbirds of cobwebs and floss, are no

Storks build their nests on rooftops, towers, and steeples.

more than an inch across at the top. The largest, constructed by eagles of branches and twigs, sometimes weigh
hundreds of pounds. The nest of a bald eagle in Ohio was
twelve feet high, eight feet across, and weighed two tons
when it finally fell during a storm—along with the tree it
had stood in for 36 years.

The oldest birds' nests are those built by storks on the
rooftops, towers and steeples of some towns in northern
Europe. These storks spend the winter months in Africa.
When they return to Europe, they go back to the same
nests year after year, repairing them and sometimes en-
larging them by adding extra branches and twigs. One
nest, perched on a village rooftop in Germany, was traced

back to the year 1549. It had been in continuous use for four centuries.

African weaverbirds are often considered the most skillful nestbuilders. A male weaverbird tears a long strand from a blade of elephant grass, flies to the branch of a tree, holds one end of the strand down with his foot, and uses his beak to wrap the strand around the branch. Then he actually ties a knot. It may be a slip knot, an overhand knot, or a half-hitch, depending on the kind of weaverbird. As the knotted strand hangs down from the branch, the bird gathers more grass and begins to weave a hollow pouch with a tube-like entrance at the bottom. A partition inside the pouch keeps the eggs from falling through this entrance tube. As many as 300 strands of grass may be woven into a single nest.

Even a Boy Scout would have to practice before he could tie a knot as well as a weaverbird. Yet the weaverbird needs no practice at all, because his intricate knot-tying and pouch-weaving are instinctive. In an unusual experiment, five generations of weaverbirds were raised

African weaverbirds can tie a variety of intricate knots with no practice at all.

simple loop   spiral coil   alternately reversed winding   half hitch   overhand knot   slip knot

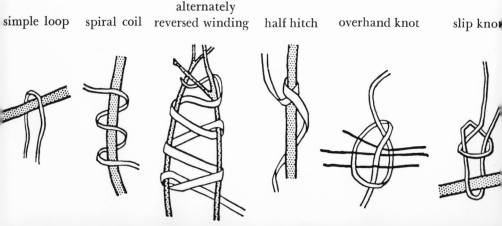

by canary foster parents in bowl-shaped canary nests. Members of the fifth generation were then provided with grass and were allowed to build nests of their own. They did not attempt to imitate the canary nests in which they had been hatched and raised. Instead, they tied perfect weaverbird knots and made perfect weaverbird nests, without making any mistakes.

Is a bird planning ahead when it builds its nest? Does it know what the nest will be used for? Probably not. Birds, along with other animals, start building their nests automatically as sex hormones enter their bloodstreams during the mating season. If a bird is injected with hormones at the wrong time of year, it will start its nest immediately —even in the dead of winter.

Under natural conditions, nestbuilding begins shortly before the female is ready to lay her eggs. The mere sight of the nest, as it slowly takes shape, can increase the flow of hormones inside the female's body. Often, she lays her first egg just as soon as the nest is finished.

Many mammals do not need nests. When a monkey, a lioness, or an elephant is ready to give birth, she simply retires to a quiet, sheltered place. A rabbit is more particular. She digs a hole in high grass or beneath some shrubbery and lines the hole with bits of fur which she plucks from her breast and abdomen. After giving birth and raising her litter, she abandons her nest.

European badgers build elaborate burrows and live in them all year long. A typical burrow is occupied by a large family group and has several entrances, emergency exits, air vents, a network of tunnels, and special chambers for sleeping, nesting, and food storage. Badgers constantly repair and enlarge their burrows and pass them on from one generation to the next.

Underground burrows of one sort or another are built by a variety of small mammals, including woodchucks, foxes, prairie dogs, and skunks. A few mammals construct shelters above the ground. Some squirrels build ball-shaped nests of twigs high in the branches of trees and line the interiors of these nests with moss and slivers of bark. In the southwest United States, the dusky-footed wood rat uses branches, leaves, and plant debris to build its nest at the base of a tree. Shaped like an upside-down ice-cream cone, these shelters are sometimes taller than a man and may contain several rooms connected by narrow passageways.

PROJECT

Investigate the Behavior
of Small Burrowing Animals

For this project you will need a breeding pair of hamsters or gerbils. In their natural habitat, these animals dig underground burrows with interlocking tunnels and chambers. The female makes her nest and raises her young in one of these chambers. Hamsters and gerbils available in pet shops have been raised in captivity for many generations. Yet when given an opportunity, they will instinctively dig burrows typical of those dug by wild members of their species.

1. Be sure to obtain a booklet of instructions for the proper care and feeding of your animals. You can buy such a booklet at almost any pet shop.

2. To observe your animals construct underground burrows, assemble a burrowing chamber similar to the one in

the drawing. Place a large glass tank (20 gallons or more) on a sturdy table near a window. Invert a smaller glass tank and lower it into the larger one. There should be about 3 or 4 inches of space between the glass of the two tanks. The flat surface of the smaller tank provides an ideal place for the animals' daily feeding.

3. Fill the space between the two tanks with soil, leaving the top third of the tank empty, as shown. Be careful not to

crack the glass as you press the soil into place. Do not use sand or other loose soil that is likely to cave in when the animals begin to build their burrow. A rich top soil that can be tightly packed is best. Place a cover with plenty of air holes over the large tank.

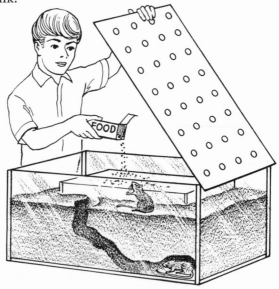

4. After a few days you will find that your animals have constructed a number of tunnels. Eventually they will build a chamber at the end of one tunnel to use as a nesting place. If you provide them with a few scraps of paper, they will probably carry the scraps to the nesting chamber and shred them into a mass of soft bedding.

5. After a while, the female is likely to give birth to a litter of five or more young. When this happens, the male should be removed from the tank; under the artificial conditions of captivity, he may attack and kill the young.

6. As you watch the female care for her young, you will observe a variety of behavioral responses that are probably innate. Make a descriptive list of these responses. Watch the

female as she nurses her young. How does her behavior aid the young in obtaining food? Does the female lick her young? What purpose do you think this serves?

7. Keep a record of the young's behavior as they mature. At what age do they begin to crawl out of the nest? How does the mother retrieve a youngster which has wandered away from the nest? How old are the young before they begin to play together? At what age do they begin to build burrows of their own?

Aside from man, however, the most expert architects among mammals are beavers. These animals fell trees with their sharp teeth and build dams across marshes and streams by floating the timber into position and cementing it together with mud and stones. A beaver dam may be as high as 12 feet and as long as 100 yards. It forms an artificial pond where the beavers construct their timber and mud lodges safely away from shore. The entrance to a lodge is always concealed beneath the water, while the network of dams maintains a constant water level and keeps the beaver pond from freezing solid during the winter.

A beaver colony usually consists of an adult male and female along with their last two litters. When the female is ready to give birth again, the male takes the youngsters, moves out of the main lodge, and sets up housekeeping in a smaller lodge not far away. The female remains in the main lodge with her infants until they are weaned. When the young males of the colony reach maturity, they leave home, find mates, and start new colonies of their own.

The dams and lodges of a beaver colony appear to be impressive examples of intelligent planning and engi-

Beaver dam: beavers float the timber into position and cement it together with mud and stones.

Beaver lodge under construction: the entrance to a lodge is always concealed underwater.

neering. Yet recent studies suggest that the building activities of beavers, like those of other mammals, are for the most part innate and automatic. Beavers, it seems, have an irresistible urge to obstruct running water. They will continue to build new dams even when the dams are unnecessary, offer no advantage to the colony, and do little more than flood the surrounding area. Beavers will also work tirelessly to repair and rebuild dams which are already in excellent condition. In New York State, some beavers made their home in an artificial lake created by a man-made dam, built of mortar and stone. This dam needed no improvement, yet the beavers worked all summer "repairing" it with mud and branches—just as if they had built it themselves.

The Care and Protection of Eggs

With two exceptions, all mammals give birth to live young. The exceptions are the duck-billed platypus and the spiny anteater, both of which lay eggs. In her grass-lined burrow, a female platypus lays two or three eggs with soft, sticky shells. Then she incubates the eggs like a bird, curling her furry body tightly around them until her infants hatch two weeks later.

The eggs of birds must also receive exacting care if they are to hatch successfully. If they are not protected, their fragile shells may crack. And if they are not kept at the right temperature, the delicate embryos may die before they have a chance to develop.

Most birds protect their eggs and keep them warm by sitting on them, or brooding. What compels an inexperienced bird to sit on her first batch of eggs? Once again, hormones are responsible. During the nesting season, hormones cause a bird to shed some of her breast feathers, exposing a patch of naked skin. Beneath this broodpatch, the blood vessels swell and enlarge. As a result, the broodpatch becomes hot and sensitive, and the uncom-

fortable bird settles down on her eggs mainly to keep
cool. If the male bird shares the task of incubating the
eggs, or sits on them by himself, then he develops a broodpatch.

Does a bird recognize its own eggs? Some songbirds will
refuse to sit on cowbird eggs which have been left in their
nests. They seem to know that the cowbird eggs are not
quite like their own. However, most small birds will accept the strange eggs of a cowbird without hesitation.

For the most part, birds are stimulated to brood by almost any eggs or egg-like objects they find in their nests.
In various experiments, birds have sat willingly on
wooden eggs, light bulbs, and door knobs. Apparently, it
is the nest itself they recognize, and not the eggs. If a herring gull's eggs are removed from its nest and are placed
on the ground about a foot away, the gull will usually
hesitate and look back and forth from its eggs to its empty
nest. Then it will settle down in its nest again, leaving its
eggs untended.

Normally, birds must sit on their eggs almost constantly. When a female broods alone, she may take brief
feeding breaks lasting a few minutes at most, or her mate
may bring her food. When a male and female take turns
in the nest, they often engage in elaborate ceremonies before changing the guard. These nest-relief ceremonies are
necessary because a brooding bird tends to attack any
other bird that approaches its nest. Before a sitting bird
will leave its eggs, its mate must identify itself and signify
its good intentions. A turnstone does this by bringing its
brooding mate a gift. The bird finds a pebble and drops it
just outside its nest. When its mate picks up the pebble

Karl W. Kenyon from National Audubon Society

Hello in there! This albatross is "talking" to its egg. Scientists call this "yapping" behavior. When these birds return to their nest after feeding, they always announce their arrival by "yapping" before they resume incubation.

and places it among the eggs, the two turnstones change places.

A few birds care for their eggs without actually sitting on them. In Australia, the male mallee fowl builds an incubator nest out of rotting vegetation which he has piled together and covered with soil. As the vegetation decays, it gives off heat. The mallee fowl uses his beak as a thermometer. He pokes his beak into the middle of the pile and tests the temperature. If the temperature isn't exactly right, he immediately makes an adjustment by adding more soil or by removing some.

Working many hours a day, the mallee fowl manages with the aid of his sensitive beak to keep the inside of his nest at an even 92 degrees. The female spends most of her time watching him work. About once a week he allows her to approach the nest and lay another egg inside. And if he is having trouble maintaining the right temperature, he may let her help out for awhile.

A pair of mallee fowl usually maintain their nest for several months. When the chicks begin to hatch—one by one every week or so—they dig their way out of the nest without assistance from their parents and dash into the Australian bush, where they disappear to fend for themselves. Despite the exacting care these birds lavish on their incubator nests, no mallee fowl has ever been seen with a brood of chicks.

Unlike birds, reptiles are cold-blooded animals. As a result, they have special problems keeping their eggs warm. A lizard called the skink solves the problem by basking in the sun until its body grows hot; then it scurries over to its nesting place and warms its eggs. Crocodiles and turtles bury their eggs in the sand. Snakes may deposit their eggs in warm mud, beneath rotting vegetation on the forest floor, or in the humid darkness of hol-

A mallee fowl incubator nest in Australia. The eggs are buried in this huge mound of soil and rotting vegetation.

Australian News and Information Bureau

Australian News and Information Bureau

A pair of mallee fowl on their nesting mound. The male keeps the inside of the nest at an even 92 degrees.

low logs. Some snakes brood their eggs, coiling their bodies around them and making shuddering movements to generate a little warmth. Others retain their eggs inside their bodies and give birth to live young.

The American alligator uses the same brooding technique as the Australian mallee fowl. She scrapes together a pile of mud and decaying vegetation, and deposits her eggs inside. Unlike most nest-building reptiles, however, she guards her nest until the eggs hatch and stays with the baby alligators until they are nearly a year old.

Insects often lay their eggs in concealed places or on a source of food, such as a leaf. Solitary bees seal their eggs in underground burrows, along with a supply of honey-moistened pollen, or "beesbread," for the larvae to eat when they hatch. A female earwig also digs an underground nest, but unlike the solitary bee, she stays close beside her developing eggs, constantly taking them into her mouth and licking them. This licking is essential if the eggs are to hatch successfully. Ants also tend their eggs by licking them, while a queen bumblebee sits on her eggs like a brooding hen, protecting them from the cold. Her brooding instinct is so strong, she will sit on small pebbles or grains of sand if her own eggs are taken away.

Although most fish abandon their eggs, a few provide intensive care for both their eggs and their young. A male stickleback chases away the female after she spawns and guards his nest until the eggs hatch a month later. He ventilates the eggs by fanning them with his tail and fins, keeping the water around them fresh, and he repairs parts of the nest that float away. In much the same way, a Siamese fighting fish dismisses the female after mating, stays close beside his nest of floating bubbles while the eggs are developing, and keeps busy replacing bubbles that break. Fighting fish and sticklebacks also make conscientious fathers, for they protect their newly hatched fry until the little fish are old enough to swim off on their own. A stickleback chases his youngsters if they wander too far from home and carries them back to the nest in his mouth.

Some fish are called "mouthbreeders" because one of the parents takes the eggs into its mouth as soon as they are laid and keeps them there until they hatch. A male sea catfish holds as many as 50 eggs, the size of small marbles, in his mouth for a month or so, and goes entirely without food while the eggs are developing. This method of tending eggs has been adopted by a number of species. In some cases, the little fry stay with their parents after hatching, and in times of danger, rush back into the safety of their parent's mouth.

This male catfish will guard his newly hatched fry until they are old enough to swim off on their own.

Animal Parents

Fish that care for their young are unusual, but the beautiful jewel fish is rare indeed because both parents cooperate in raising their family. These popular aquarium fish have been studied by Dr. Konrad Lorenz, a distinguished Austrian scientist and one of the founders of ethology—the science of animal behavior.

While jewel fish are developing, both parents guard the eggs and fan a continuous stream of fresh water towards them. After the fry hatch, they lay quietly in their nesting hollow at first. Before long, they begin to swim, and for several weeks their parents keep them together and lead them through the water.

These exploratory journeys take place during the day. In the evening, the parents lead their youngsters back to the family's nesting hollow. The mother jewel fish hovers above the nest and calls to her fry by jerking her glittering fins up and down. The youngsters cluster around her and then descend into the nest for the night. The father, meanwhile, searches for stragglers. If he finds one, he scoops the straggler into his mouth, swims back to the nesting hollow, and blows the infant into its night-time nursery.

Dr. Lorenz once witnessed an unforgettable scene as a father jewel fish was putting his fry to bed for the night: "I came, late one evening, into the laboratory. It was already dusk and I wished hurriedly to feed a few fishes which had not received anything to eat that day; amongst them was a pair of jewel fishes who were tending their young. As I approached the container, I saw that most of the young were already in the nesting hollow over which the mother was hovering. She refused to come for food when I threw pieces of earthworm into the tank. The father, however, who, in great excitement, was dashing backwards and forwards searching for truants, allowed himself to be diverted from his duty by a nice hind-end of earthworm. He swam up and seized the worm, but, owing to its size, was unable to swallow it. As he was in the act of chewing this mouthful, he saw a baby fish swimming by itself across the tank; he started as though stung, raced after the baby and took it into his already filled mouth.

"It was a thrilling moment. The fish had in its mouth two different things of which one must go into the stomach and the other into the nest. What would he do? I must confess that, at that moment, I would not have given twopence for the life of that tiny jewel fish. But wonderful

what really happened! The fish stood stock still with full
cheeks, but did not chew. If ever I have seen a fish think,
it was in that moment. . . .

"For many seconds the father jewel fish stood riveted
and one could almost see how his feelings were working.
Then he solved the conflict in a way for which one was
bound to feel admiration: he spat out the whole contents
of his mouth: the worm fell to the bottom, and the little
jewel fish . . . did the same. Then the father turned reso-
lutely to the worm and ate it up, without haste but all the
time with one eye on the child which 'obediently' lay on
the bottom beneath him. When he had finished, he in-
haled the baby and carried it home to its mother.

"Some students, who had witnessed the whole scene,
started as one man to applaud."

Ordinarily, a fish's responses are controlled by instinct.
But in this remarkable scene, two conflicting urges were
reconciled with what appeared to be an intelligent deci-
sion. Perhaps it was.

Among insects, family life is limited mainly to the social bees, wasps, ants and termites. In fact, the main busi-
ness of an insect society is to bring up a new generation.

As eggs hatch in a honey-bee hive, nurse bees take
charge of the worm-like larvae, feeding them honey and
pollen along with a nutritious fluid secreted by the nurse
bees' glands. Since a single fast-growing larva consumes
about 1300 meals a day, the nurse bees have plenty to do.
After six days, a fully developed larva is sealed inside its
cell where it spins a silken cocoon, changes into an adult

bee, and finally bites its way out of the cell to join the busy life of the hive.

Ants, termites, and social wasps also protect, handle, clean, and feed their developing young. Paper wasps capture insects, tear them to pieces, chew them up, and feed this predigested mash to their hungry larvae. Ants lick their larvae to keep them clean, feed them the same kind of food eaten by the rest of the colony, and in some species carry the larvae with them on hunting expeditions.

Infant care among insects is a rigidly organized, massproduction affair. Among birds and mammals, however, family life usually involves a close personal relationship between parents and their offspring.

Chicks, ducklings, goslings, and other ground fowl are able to run about and peck for food soon after they hatch. Even so, they never wander far from the protective wings of their mother and will instinctively follow her wherever she goes. The urge to follow is very strong in newly hatched ground fowl. If for some reason the mother bird is not there, the chicks may follow the first moving object they see. Dr. Konrad Lorenz hatched some goslings in an incubator, and since he was the first moving thing they

A caspian tern and her newly hatched chick.

Hugh M. Halliday

saw, they began to run after him. After following him for a short time, they refused to follow anything else. As far as the goslings were concerned, Dr. Lorenz was their "mother goose."

Most birds are blind, featherless, and completely helpless when they come into the world. If they are to survive, they must be fed and protected. Feeding can be quite a job for the parents, since an infant songbird has an insatiable appetite and may consume its own weight in food every 24 hours. A pair of wrens, feeding five or six nestlings, will make 300 trips a day to their nest. Every few minutes, one of the parents arrives with more insects and stuffs them into the nestlings' gaping mouths.

To a parent bird, a gaping mouth is an irresistible feeding signal. In many species, the mouths and throats of nestlings have vivid colors and markings which seem to intensify the parent's feeding urge. As we have seen, a parent bird will spend all day gathering food and stuffing it into a wooden model that is shaped and colored like the gaping mouths of the parent's own nestlings.

An infant bird's gaping response is just as automatic as its parent's feeding behavior. Day-old nestlings will gape for food as soon as they hear their parents coming or feel them land on the nest. If an observer taps the nest lightly with his finger, the little birds will lift their heads and gape—waiting to be fed.

Newly hatched herring gulls get their first meal by pecking at a red spot near the tip of their parent's bill. Dr. Niko Tinbergen has described this behavior:

"The parent stands up and looks down into the nest, and then we may see the first begging behavior of the

young. They do not lose time in contemplating or study-
ing the parent, whose head they see for the first time, but
begin to peck at its bill-tip right away, with repeated,
quick, and relatively well-aimed darts of their tiny bills.
They usually spread their wings and utter a faint squeaking sound. The old bird cannot resist this, and if only the
chicks persist it will feed them. . . .

"All at once the parent bends its head down and regur-
gitates an enormous lump of half-digested food. This is
dropped, and a small piece is now picked up again and
presented to the chicks. These redouble their efforts, and
soon get hold of the food, whereupon the parent presents
them with a new morsel. . . . After the chicks have had
one or two turns, they cease to respond and with an amaz-
ing promptness they fade away into a peaceful slum-
ber. . . .

"One never gets tired of watching these first reactions
of the chicks to their parents. Their remarkable 'know-
how,' not dependent on experience of any kind but entirely innate, never fails to impress one as an instance of
the adaptedness of an inborn response."

Another inborn response helps protect a herring gull
chick from danger. This response first appears even before the chick hatches. Inside its shell, it can be heard
squeaking faintly, but the moment its parents sound an
alarm call, the unhatched chick falls silent. After hatching, it crouches silently in its nest when it hears this call.
When it is a day old, it runs out of the nest and crouches
a short distance away. And as it grows a bit older, it se-
lects a special hiding place to use when the alarm is
sounded.

Adult members of the colony fly into the air as soon as an alarm is sounded. One by one, they swoop down on any predator who threatens their young and strike him with their legs if he approaches a nest. Sometimes the attacking birds "bomb" an enemy with regurgitated food or body waste.

Parent birds often risk their lives to defend their young. A goose hisses fearlessly at an enemy. A turkey jumps menacingly towards an intruder, her wings flapping and her claws extended. A killdeer hops across the ground dragging a "broken" wing, calling attention to herself and away from her nestlings. As the enemy approaches, the "crippled" killdeer suddenly flies into the air and escapes. Several other birds also pretend to be injured when their young are threatened. No one knows how this behavior began, yet it is clearly innate. A mother killdeer will display a "broken" wing the first time her nest is threatened, even though she has never seen another bird behave like this.

Mammals feed their young with milk produced by the mother's mammary glands. The young are born alive after developing inside the mother's body.

When a mother mammal gives birth, she begins to lick the birth fluids from the infant's fur. This licking is essential, for it stimulates the infant to take its first breath. A mother sea lion follows a different procedure. After giving birth on a beach, she dunks her infant into the sea, stimulating it to breath. A mother dolphin gives birth under the water and then pushes her infant to the surface for its first breath. While she is doing this, other dolphins

William M. Stephens

A dolphin mother and her two-day-old infant.

gather around and keep up an excited chorus of whistles, yelps, wails, and squeaks.

A baby dolphin can swim beside its mother as soon as it is born. Grazing animals, such as cows, horses and deer, struggle to their feet shortly after birth and begin to follow their mother and the rest of the herd. Most mammals are born helpless and blind, however, and must be carried about by their mother. A kitten cannot crawl around on its own until it is three or four weeks old. Until then, the mother carries her kittens with her teeth. Monkeys carry their infants in their arms, and when the youngsters are a little older, they ride on their mother's back.

Since mammals have the most highly developed brains of any animals, learning plays an important role in their lives. A lion cub must learn many of the tricks and techniques of hunting, for example. It does so by accompanying its parents on hunting expeditions. At first, the cub takes no part in the hunt, but simply stands aside and watches. By the time it is nine or ten months old, it knows how to stalk its prey, keeping downwind and out of sight. Now it may capture and kill small animals, but it still lacks the speed and skill of an adult. The cub's education must continue for another year or so before it is ready to leave home and make its own living.

Of all young animals, none have more to learn than the primates—the monkeys and apes. By watching its mother, a young primate learns which plants to eat and which to avoid. By running, chasing, climbing, and wrestling with its playmates, it masters the skills it will need to survive as an adult. By observing older males and females, it learns the rules by which members of its society live.

An African elephant helps her young calf climb a steep bank.

Courtesy of Renton Cowley

Soon after birth, an infant monkey or ape begins to recognize its mother and hold out its arms to her. And the mother's whole life centers about her baby at least until it is weaned. She holds the infant as it clings to her. She cleans and inspects its body, strokes its fur, murmurs to it, and crouches over it at night to protect it from cold and rain. A mother gorilla will not allow her infant to wander more than a few feet away until the youngster is five or six months old. She nurses her baby until it is a year-and-a-half old, and sleeps with it by her side until it is nearly three.

The maternal drive is strong among all mammals—so strong, in fact, that a female deprived of the chance to have young of her own will sometimes "adopt" other young animals. This happened recently in Van Buren, Arkansas, when a pet dog named "Fistie" adopted four baby chicks. Shortly after the chicks hatched, Fistie shepherded them into her kitchen box and allowed them to snuggle up to her. When the chicks grew restless and

Fistie and her feathered brood.

Crawford County Courier, *Van Buren, Ark.*

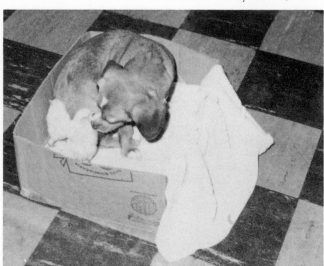

If the chicks wandered too far away, Fistie picked them up and carried them back to her box.

climbed out of the box, Fistie watched them carefully. And if they strayed too far away, the dog picked them up gently with her teeth and carried them back to the box.

When a newspaper photographer came to take pictures of Fistie, the dog growled fiercely at this stranger and would not let him approach her feathered brood.

7.

Blueprint for Survival

Crawling out of the ocean onto the beach, a green sea turtle presses her snout against the wet sand and searches for some reassuring sign that she has reached the right place. Then she looks up, and as she peers into the distance, her head darts nervously back and forth.

For several minutes she waits at the water's edge. Finally, she starts moving again. Dragging her massive body to a point high on the beach, she finds a sheltered spot behind a dune and begins to scoop out a nesting hole in the sand.

As soon as the nest is ready, the turtle starts to fill it with her eggs. Heaving great sighs, and weeping salty tears which wash the sand from her eyes, she lays about 100 eggs in all. When she is finished, she covers her nest and attempts to conceal it, using her powerful flippers to scatter sand and debris over the site. Finally, she crawls back down the beach, plunges into the surf, and disappears.

Hundreds of other green turtles will dig nests on the same isolated stretch of beach in the days ahead, and each nest will be filled with about 100 eggs. Buried in the warm sand, the eggs will incubate for nearly two months. Though the beach seems quiet during this period, ani-

Female green turtle on nesting beach.

mals that prey on baby turtles are already gathering here.

Beyond the dunes, a coyote sniffs the ground. A wild cat prowls silently through the coastal scrub not far away. Near shore, a ghost crab snaps its vise-like claws, while overhead, buzzards circle.

At last, the eggs begin to hatch. In each nest, 100 baby turtles break out of their shells and start to squirm their way up to the surface. Usually, they emerge at night in a wriggling mass of tiny shells and thrashing flippers. All across the beach, nests erupt like small volcanoes, spilling hatchlings onto the sand where their enemies are waiting.

"The little turtles come out into a world eager to eat them," writes Dr. Archie Carr, a University of Florida zoologist and a sea turtle expert. "They have to go fast and straight toward the ocean even though they can't see it, never saw it before, and know of its existence only as a set of signals to react to instinctively. It seems a little odd —the mother turtle leaving the new generation in such a predicament."

Many of the nests are behind sand dunes which hide the ocean from view. Rocks, driftwood and other obstacles block the turtles' path. Even so, the hatchlings flip-flop rapidly across the beach toward the sea, like toys that have been wound up and headed in the right direction.

No one knows what guides them. Some experiments suggest that they may be attracted by light reflected from the ocean. But the actual signal to which they respond remains a mystery. Whatever it is, their lives depend on the instinct that makes them race headlong toward the sea. If a hatchling hesitates, it may be plucked from the sand by a buzzard. If it goes in the wrong direction, it may be gobbled up by a hungry coyote.

Many of the hatchlings never make it across the beach, but those that do disappear immediately into the ocean. As yet, little is known about the turtles during their first months at sea. They seem to be carried by ocean currents to their traditional feeding grounds, which may be hundreds of miles away. After a few years, when they reach maturity, they swim back to the same beaches where they were born. Like their parents before them, they lay their eggs in the sand and pass on to their offspring the hereditary blueprints that made it possible for them to survive.

Blueprints from the Past

How can a pattern of behavior be passed along from one

generation to the next? Actually, it is not behavior itself which is inherited, but the *physical equipment* that makes behavior possible.

A baby turtle inherits a particular kind of brain and nervous system from its parents—just as it inherits its muscles, glands and sense organs, its strong flippers, leathery skin, and hard shell. This physical equipment is organized in such a way that the turtle will respond automatically to certain signals.

One such signal seems to come from the sea. Picked up by the turtle's eyes, the signal is translated into nerve impulses which are relayed to special centers in the brain. Processing this information, the brain transmits new impulses to muscles in the turtle's front flippers and hind legs. The muscles go into action, and the turtle starts moving toward the sea.

An animal's behavior is determined by the design of its body—especially by the organization of its nervous system. A turtle is "pre-wired" at birth to behave like others of its kind. We do not yet fully understand how complex patterns of behavior can be built into an animal's nervous system. However, recent discoveries have revealed the nature of the genetic code through which all living things inherit their body design from previous generations.

Heredity is a form of communication with the past. If you say that you have "inherited" your father's nose or your mother's eyes, you don't mean that the organs themselves were passed along like hand-me-downs. You mean that your nose is shaped like your father's, or that your eyes are the same color as your mother's. What was passed

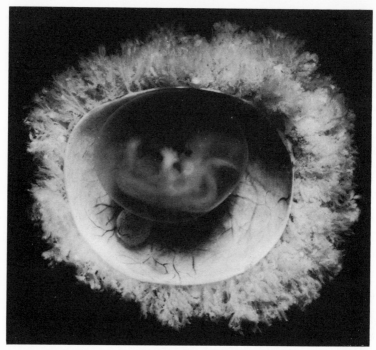

A five-week-old human embryo. Genes provide the blueprint for body design.

down were the instructions your body needed to produce a nose of a certain shape, or eyes of a certain color.

These hereditary instructions are called *genes* and are contained within every male sperm cell and every female egg cell. When a sperm and egg unite to form a new life, genes provide the developing embryo with a detailed blueprint for building a body with certain definite characteristics.

How can complex hereditary instructions be stored within microscopic sperm and egg cells? We know today that genes are composed of a chemical substance called *deoxyribonucleic acid,* or *DNA* for short. A single molecule of DNA is too small to be seen with the most powerful microscope. By using X-ray techniques, however, scientists have been able to determine the physical structure of these DNA molecules, which contain within them one of the fundamental secrets of life.

A DNA molecule looks like a tiny twisted ladder. The rungs of the ladder are made up of four different chemicals which occur in various combinations. Like the dots and dashes of the Morse Code, the order and arrangement of these chemicals spell out the information the body needs to produce all its inherited traits.

In other words, genetic information is transmitted by a chemical code. It is DNA with its chemical code that is passed along from one generation to the next.

DNA is found in the cells of all animals and plants. In every case, its chemical composition is about the same. The chief difference is the order in which the chemicals occur on the rungs of the DNA ladder. A ladder-shaped molecule may have as many as 20,000 rungs. Thousands of these molecules can be found in a single cell. As a result, a cell may contain millions of chemically coded messages which together make up the genes.

A complete set of genes is contained in the cell from which every living thing develops. These chemical instructions determine if that particular cell will become a man, an insect, or a potato. They determine also the shape of an individual's nose, the color of his eyes, the texture of his hair, and thousands of other physical characteristics.

A remarkable feature of DNA molecules is that they can make copies of themselves. In all living things, the cells are constantly dividing, and as this happens, the ladder-shaped DNA molecules also divide. Each ladder splits in half and then rebuilds itself. In this way, all the information coded in the original DNA that we inherit from our parents is duplicated for every cell of our body. And when we produce offspring of our own, copies of our DNA are transmitted to our children.

Each individual receives half his DNA blueprint from his father and half from his mother. As a result, he is not exactly like either parent but is a unique mixture of the traits he has inherited from both. Since the possible combinations of genes are almost unlimited, we can see great differences among brothers and sisters in the same family. Like his fingerprints, each individual is different in some way from every other individual on earth.

This is true of all animals. In a litter of puppies, each puppy may have different markings, as well as other differences not easily seen. Hunters have found litters of fox pups ranging in color from brownish red to silver gray. These natural variations result from different combinations of genes passed down from the parents to their young.

Occasionally, a new trait appears which results from a *mutation*—a sudden change in the genes. The first silver coat that ever appeared among fox pups was caused by a mutation which altered the genes that determine fur color. Since mutations affect the genetic blueprint itself, the new traits they produce can be passed down to further generations, and today many fox pups are born with silver-gray fur.

Mutations can occur among all living things. They may be caused by radiation penetrating the cells of the body,

A DNA molecule resembles a tiny twisted ladder. Each rung of the ladder consists of two chemicals: *adenine* linked to *thymine,* or *guanine* linked to *cytosine.* The order and arrangement of these four chemicals determines the genetic code of every living cell.

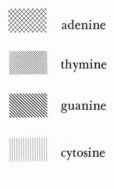

adenine

thymine

guanine

cytosine

by high temperatures, and by various other factors. Wingless flies result from a mutation which has apparently destroyed the genetic blueprint for the production of wings.

Though the causes of mutations were not understood until quite recently, stock-breeders have long been familiar with the sudden appearance of new and unusual traits in animals. About two centuries ago, on a New England farm owned by Seth Wright, a ram was born with short, oddly shaped legs. Starting with this ram, Wright raised a special breed of short-legged sheep, useful because they could not jump over the low stone fences of New England. Hornless cattle, which are also mutants, are desirable to stock-breeders because they cannot gore each other or their keepers.

Inborn patterns of behavior can also be affected by mutations. On a tropical beach which had been exposed to heavy doses of radiation as a result of atomic testing, sea turtles lost their instinctive sense of direction. The genetic blueprint that guided them to the sea had apparently been destroyed, and they wandered aimlessly back and forth across the beach, unable to find their way.

Natural Selection

In the far north, where snow blankets the earth for many months of the year, a silver fox stalks its prey. Camouflaged against the white landscape, this animal is far more successful as a hunter than its red-coated relatives would be.

Farther south, where snow seldom falls, a silver coat would be a distinct disadvantage. Here, among the brown leaves and rocks of the forest floor, the darker coat of the red fox provides effective camouflage.

On the North American continent, foxes of the same species have blueprints for the production of red coats, silver coats, and even coats that contain a mixture of red and silver hairs. In each region of the continent, however, the most successful foxes are those best suited to blend with their surroundings. Silver is the most common coat color of foxes living in the north. Red is by far the most common color in the south. Between these two regions, where summers and winters are more nearly the same length, we find many foxes with mixed coats, composed of both red and silver hair.

For the most part, an animal's natural surroundings determine which characteristics will be favorable and which will be unfavorable to the animal's survival. An animal with favorable characteristics is more likely to survive and transmit its genetic blueprints to the next generation. This is what we mean by *natural selection*.

To demonstrate how certain characteristics are selected by nature, we can set up a simple laboratory experiment. To begin with, we place some flying insects in a wire cage and give them enough food to live and breed for many generations. Most of the insects in our cage have normal wings. A few are wingless mutants. It is not uncommon to find such mutants in an insect population.

Wings are a definite advantage to individuals which live in areas where winds are not too strong and where food is scattered. Under these conditions, those insects that can fly are more likely to survive and reproduce than wingless mutants. In our experiment, however, flying will be a disadvantage. Using a large fan, we shall direct a constant stream of air through the cage. Most of the insects that try to fly will be blown against the wall of the cage and will perish. The wingless mutants, meanwhile, will do quite well. Crawling about on the bottom of the cage, they will feed with little competition and will multiply in number, passing their wingless body design on to their offspring. Though we started our experiment with a majority of winged insects, after a few generations the population in our cage will be made up largely of flightless individuals.

Apparently, something like this has actually happened in nature. A small island in the Indian Ocean is constantly swept by savage winds. Flying insects that came to this island in the distant past were unable to survive, and today the island is populated only by wingless mutants.

Man has been able to imitate the process of natural selection in his breeding of domestic animals. For thousands of years he has picked from his flocks and herds those individuals with the most desirable traits. From the wild horse he has developed high-spirited racehorses and the gentle shetland pony. From the jungle fowl he has bred prized egg-laying poultry. Through careful selection he has created special breeds of sheep which grow fine wool, hogs which yield lean meat, cows which produce large volumes of milk.

The remarkable variety of dogs that exist today, from the toy poodle to the great dane, are also the product of selective breeding. Some dogs have been bred for their hunting ability, others for their intelligence, their sensitivity, or their affection. These animals have been selected as much for their *behavior* as for their physical characteristics.

Scientists believe that a similar process in nature has shaped the behavior as well as the body design of all animals. For many millions of years, individuals of each species have struggled to find food, reproduce their own kind, and protect themselves from danger. They have

Evelyn M. Shafer

The remarkable variety of dogs that exist today are the products of selective breeding.

struggled to survive, and those who behaved in ways best suited to their environment were the ones who survived long enough to pass the same behavior patterns on to their offspring.

Dr. Niko Tinbergen has described this process at work in a colony of gulls. Normally, both male and female gulls have a brooding instinct and share the task of sitting on their eggs. This gives both parents a chance to stretch their legs and find food. However, Dr. Tinbergen observed one male gull who seemed to have no brooding urge. This male never relieved his mate by taking his turn on the nest. The female persevered heroically. She sat on her eggs continuously for twenty days. On the twenty-first day, the starving female finally deserted her nest, and the brood was lost. "However disastrous this was for the young," Dr. Tinbergen observed, "it was a blessing for the species, for what if the offspring had inherited this defect from the father?"

The behavior of the eyed hawk moth also seems to have been shaped by natural selection. This insect has a brightly colored pattern, resembling a pair of large eyes, on its lower wings. When the moth is resting on a branch or the trunk of a tree, its eye spots are hidden beneath its folded outer wings. But if the moth is disturbed, it immediately spreads its wings and exposes its eye spots. When a hungry bird pecks at one of these insects, the sudden display of eye spots makes it appear as if the bird has confronted one of its deadly enemies, such as a cat or an owl.

Experiments have shown how effective these eye spots can be in protecting eyed hawk moths from birds. When a blue jay was placed in a cage with a moth, the bird approached the insect and started to peck at it. Spreading its wings, the moth revealed its eye spots. The startled blue jay jumped high into the air, hit the roof of the cage, and refused to go near the moth again.

This display behavior has helped the eyed hawk moth survive as a species. Yet each generation of young must meet the standards nature requires. If an individual moth doesn't spread its wings wide enough or quickly enough, or if it fails to spread them at all, it will wind up inside a bird's stomach and will never become the parent of a new generation.

Behavior and Survival

Innate patterns of behavior are an essential part of an animal's equipment for survival. If baby turtles were not instinctively drawn to the sea, their species would become extinct. If a migratory bird was not equipped with a built-in flight plan, its journey might end in disaster. The

Eyed hawk moth: when disturbed, the moth raises its outer wings, revealing red and blue eye-spots on its lower wings.

ready-made responses of inborn behavior make it possible for an animal to perform acts it has neither the time, the ability, nor the opportunity to learn.

A barn swallow does not have to explore the earth or

consult weather charts before it finds a place where the seasons are right for breeding and where there is plenty of food. A rabbit doesn't have to learn from experience that overcrowding might threaten its survival; the rabbit automatically safeguards its food supply and nesting site by defending a private territory. No one teaches a firefly how to attract a mate, a wasp how to build a nest, or an eyed hawk moth how to defend itself. These acts are all controlled by instinct.

Though the instinct for self-preservation is strong, the instinct to preserve the species is even stronger. Migrating salmon overcome staggering obstacles as they return to their spawning grounds, where they lay their eggs and die. Animals whose young are born helpless often risk their own lives to protect their offspring. With shrieks and dashes, a robin takes an almost suicidal stand as she attempts to drive away the prowling cat that threatens her nest.

Innate patterns of behavior are an essential part of an animal's equipment for survival. Ruffed grouse chicks "freeze" motionless when danger threatens.

Hugh M. Halliday

Yet a bird who instinctively endangers her life for her young will let one of her nestlings starve if it falls accidentally out of the nest. She has no built-in response to deal with this situation. Instinct tells her to stuff the mouths inside her nest; she is blind to other gaping mouths, even if they belong to her own young and are only a short distance away.

When a cowbird, a cuckoo, or some other parasitic bird is hatched and raised by foster parents, it often pushes its foster brothers and sisters out of the nest. The victims usually fall to the ground, but occasionally, one is left lying on the edge of the nest. With a simple movement of her beak, the mother bird could tip the helpless infant back to safety, yet instinct has not equipped her to perform this act. She lets the nestling die of cold and hunger before her eyes—apparently without realizing what is happening.

Instinct is too inflexible to cope with every situation that may arise. In Germany a few years ago, a highway was built through a marshland where toads come to spawn each year. Like salmon, toads will lay their eggs only in the place where they themselves were born. But when these particular toads returned to their ancestral spawning grounds, they found a concrete strip instead of a muddy pond. Though other ponds suitable for spawning were not far away, the toads were unable to change the pattern of behavior passed down by their ancestors. Crawling desperately about on the highway, they were slaughtered by passing cars.

Many species have become extinct because they were unable to adjust to changes in their environment. On its comfortable island home in the Indian Ocean, the dodo bird had no natural enemies and no need to fear or flee other living creatures. Over countless generations, these birds grew fat and sluggish and even lost the ability to fly. Yet their easy life allowed them to flourish until the early 1500's, when men first began to settle on the island. The settlers brought with them dogs and pigs, and the trusting dodo was no match for these human and animal newcomers who fed on its eggs as well as its flesh. Unable to change either its flightless body or its defenseless behavior, the dodo vanished in less than 200 years.

Today, the green sea turtle may be on its way to extinction. These reptiles are valued for their meat and hides, and increased hunting in recent years has taken a heavy toll of the world's green turtle population. Despite legal restrictions, the hunting continues and the turtles are now being killed in remote places where they were not hunted before.

As long as the turtles are at sea, their great size makes them almost immune to danger. But they must come ashore to lay their eggs, exposing themselves and their offspring to the hazards of the land. For millions of years, as long as the dangers they faced were natural ones, the turtles were quite successful. From each batch of 100 turtle eggs, enough hatchlings survived to maintain the species. Now, however, the species may suffer the same fate as the dodo bird. Since the turtles cannot change their nesting behavior, they face the danger of extinction as instinct leads them back to the same beaches year after year, where armed hunters are waiting.

There is nothing new about extinction, of course.

State of Florida Development Commission

Once dangerously close to extinction, these roseate spoonbills are being re-established through conservation measures.

Countless species became extinct long before man ever appeared on earth. Gigantic dinosaurs once dominated the earth; then they vanished, unable to cope with the natural changes that occurred in their environment. In modern times, because of changes caused by man, there has been an alarming increase in the rate of extinction. At this moment, about 100 species of birds and 600 species of mammals are in imminent danger of disappearing permanently from the earth.

One species, the sea otter, helped save itself from extinction because of its ability to learn. At one time, sea otters were primarily land creatures, inhabiting island beaches at the northern edge of the Pacific Ocean. Though they were expert swimmers who lived intimately with the sea, it was mainly along the shore that they found food, slept, mated, and bore their young. Eskimos who shared the otters' islands killed a few of the animals to make clothes of their fur, but there were hundreds of thousands of sea otters then, and not many Eskimos.

Sea otters have the most exquisite fur in the world. Starting about 200 years ago, the beauty of their skins nearly resulted in their extermination. Otter furs became so valuable, hunters converged on the animals' islands from all over the world. As massive expeditions were organized, the otters began to disappear. Year after year, the desperate animals were driven from their beaches, pursued in small boats, and slaughtered ruthlessly.

In 1911, when the species was nearly extinct, the governments of the United States, Great Britain, Japan, and Russia agreed to stop all killing of sea otters. By then, however, the few surviving otters were learning to live in the safety of the sea.

They had moved from the beaches where their ancestors had lived out into the sea, making a new home for themselves in thick beds of floating kelp, or seaweed. To succeed in this environment, the otters had to learn how to find their food away from shore, and how to wrap themselves in strands of seaweed while they slept, so waves would not carry them back to the perils of the beaches they had abandoned. They had to learn how to mate and give birth amidst the dense, tangled waterplants where they had sought refuge, how to raise their young there, and how to hide.

Today, sea otters are gradually increasing their numbers again. Yet after living on land for so many genera-

Karl W. Kenyon from National Audubon Society

A mother sea otter holds her pup on her chest as both sleep.

tions, they are still adapting to their watery environment, and each young otter must learn anew the difficult art of surviving at sea.

As we have already seen, all animals can learn. However, some can learn a great deal more than others. An insect is primarily a creature of instinct: for the most part, it is locked into innate patterns of behavior which have developed over millions of years. Mammals, on the other hand, learn constantly from experience.

Of all mammals, man is the only one whose behavior depends almost entirely on learning. In fact, man's seemingly limitless ability to learn has made him the most successful living creature on earth.

No animal has been able to mold its life or environment in the way man has done. He has leveled mountains, uprooted forests, and paved the land with cities, factories, and highways. He has learned to travel through the air, live beneath the sea, fly to the moon, and bring the whole world into his living room. Having penetrated the mystery of life's genetic blueprint, man is on the threshold of controlling his heredity and shaping human destiny. And having unlocked the secret of the atom, he holds in his hands the power to transform the earth, or destroy it.

Many of the changes brought about by man have enriched his life. Others threaten his very existence. For as man has worked to reshape his environment, he has at the same time fouled the lakes and rivers essential to his survival and has poisoned the very air he breathes. Medical advances have created an exploding human population, but as yet, little has been done to overcome starvation, warfare, or racial strife.

Today, thoughtful people wonder if man can meet the challenges of the dangerous new world he has created—if he can, in fact, survive. Unlike the dodo, man has the capacity to change his old habits of behavior. And this is precisely what the human species must do if it is to prevent its own extinction.

The New York Times

Can man survive?

For Further Reading

Books

Barnett, S. A., *Instinct and Intelligence*. Englewood Cliffs, N.J., Prentice-Hall, 1967.

Berrill, J., *Wonders of Animal Migration*. New York, Dodd Mead Co., 1964.

Carrighar, S., *Wild Heritage*. Boston, Houghton Mifflin Co., 1965 (also in paperback).

Carrington, R., *The Mammals*. New York, Time-Life Books, 1963.

Carthy, J. D., *Animals and Their Ways*. New York, Natural History Press, 1965.

Cosgrove, M., *The Strange World of Animal Senses*. New York, Dodd Mead Co., 1961.

Darling, L. and Darling, L., *Bird*. Boston, Houghton Mifflin Co., 1962.

Freedman, R. and Morriss, J. E., *How Animals Learn*. New York, Holiday House, Inc., 1969.

Hutchins, R. E., *Insects*. Englewood Cliffs, N.J., Prentice-Hall, 1966.

Kaufman, J., *Wings, Sun, and Stars: The Story of Bird Migration*. New York, William Morrow Co., 1969.

Lorenz, K., *King Solomon's Ring*. New York, Thomas Y. Crowell Co., 1952 (also in paperback).

———, *Man Meets Dog*. Boston, Houghton Mifflin Co., 1955 (also in paperback).

Ommanney, F. D., *The Fishes*. New York, Time-Life Books, 1964.

Selsam, M., *Animals as Parents*. New York, William Morrow Co., 1965.

———, *The Courtship of Animals*. New York, William Morrow Co., 1964.

Silvan, J., *Raising Laboratory Animals*. New York, Natural History Press, 1966.

Simon, S., *Animals in Field and Laboratory*. New York, McGraw-Hill, 1968.

Thorpe, W. H., *Learning and Instinct in Animals*. Cambridge, Mass., Harvard University Press, 1963.

Tinbergen, N., *Animal Behavior*. New York, Time-Life Books, 1965.

———, *Curious Naturalists*. New York, Basic Books, 1958 (also in paperback).

———, *The Study of Instinct*. New York, Oxford University Press, 1951.

Magazine Articles

Alexander, R. D., "The Evolution of Cricket Chirps." *Natural History*, November, 1966.

Carr, A., "Caribbean Green Turtle: Imperiled Gift of the Sea." *National Geographic*, June, 1967.

———, "The Navigation of the Green Turtle." *Scientific American*, May, 1965.

Dugdale, B. E., "The Weaving of an Engineering Masterpiece." *Natural History*, March, 1969.

Eibl-Eibesfeldt, I., "The Fighting Behavior of Animals." *Scientific American*, December, 1961.

Emlen, J. T. and Penney, R. L., "The Navigation of Penguins." *Scientific American*, October, 1964.

Flyger, V. and Townsend, M. R., "The Migration of Polar Bears." *Scientific American*, February, 1968.

Gibson, E. J. and Walk, R. D., "The Visual Cliff." *Scientific American*, April, 1960.

Hailman, J. P., "How an Instinct Is Learned." *Scientific American*, December, 1969.

Hall, E. T., "Territorial Needs and Limits." *Natural History*, December, 1965.

Johnsgard, P. A., "Dawn Rendezvous on the Lek." *Natural History*, March, 1967.

———, "The Evolution of Duck Courtship." *Natural History*, February, 1968.

Lehrman, D. S., "The Reproductivity Behavior of Ring Doves." *Scientific American*, November, 1964.

Mykytowycz, R., "Territorial Marking by Rabbits." *Scientific American*, May, 1968.

Netboy, A., "Round Trip with the Salmon." *Natural History*, June-July, 1969.

Sauer, E. G. F., "Celestial Navigation by Birds." *Scientific American*, August, 1958.

Tinbergen, N., "The Curious Behavior of the Stickleback." *Scientific American,* December, 1954.

Wallace, A. F. C. and Lathbury, V. L., "Culture and the Beaver." *Natural History,* November, 1968.

Zahl, P. A., "Mystery of the Monarch Butterfly." *National Geographic,* April, 1963.

Index